THE
MAGIC OF
RAYS

Southwest Miami High School
8855 S. W. 50 Terrace, Miami, Fla.

THE
MAGIC OF
RAYS

BY

Johannes Dogigli

Translated from the German and Edited by

CHARLES FULLMAN

New York : Alfred·A·Knopf

1961

535
D

L. C. catalog card number: 60–15673

THIS IS A BORZOI BOOK,
PUBLISHED BY ALFRED A. KNOPF, INC.

Copyright © 1960 by Alfred A. Knopf, Inc. All rights reserved. No part of this book may be reproduced in any form without permission in writing from the publisher, except by a reviewer who may quote brief passages and reproduce not more than three illustrations in a review to be printed in a magazine or newspaper. Manufactured in the United States of America. Published simultaneously in Canada by McClelland & Stewart, Ltd.

Published January 23, 1961
Second Printing, June, 1961

Originally published in German as *Magie der Strahlen*. Copyright © 1957 by Paul List Verlag München.

Contents

12734

List of Plates

THE
MAGIC OF
RAYS

CHAPTER 1

The Miracle of Light

SEEN THROUGH Galileo's telescope, the nocturnal sky appeared studded with stars of whose existence no one until then had had the faintest inkling. The Pleiades no longer showed seven stars, but thirty-six; in the sword and belt of Orion, Galileo counted as many as eight stars; and the number of stars in the Milky Way could not be even approximately estimated. The moon was no longer a flat disk with a "face" or a "man" in it; it stood revealed as a rugged landscape pitted with craters; the deep shadows suggested high mountains. And the dark shadows that from time to time moved across the sun's surface could no longer be interpreted as clouds standing off it; they were genuine "spots."

Galileo's most revolutionary discovery began on the night of January 7, 1610, when, turning his telescope toward Jupiter, he noticed that the planet was not alone; it had companions: three tiny "stars." Two of them, he saw, were located east and one west of Jupiter. That in itself would have been no cause for excitement. On the next night, however, the three "stars" were in a different position, all west of the planet. Evidently they were moving around

Jupiter and were not "stars" but little moons. Until then the view had been held that only the earth had a moon moving around it. Here was a second *planetary system*, and Jupiter had not just one moon, but several. The prevailing conception of the special position of the earth was shattered.

Galileo hesitated for a long time before making public his observations. Would not the Church, on dogmatic grounds, take the sternest measures to prevent the spread of the inferences to be drawn from these observations?

In the meantime Galileo discovered a fourth moon circling Jupiter. (Today eleven are known; a twelfth is still the subject of some uncertainty.) The fourth moon had not been visible at the time of the first observations because at that moment it had been behind Jupiter.

We all know what happened to Galileo: at the Council of Rome in 1633 he was compelled to abjure as "absurd, philosophically false, well-nigh heretical and blasphemous" what he had defended. Galileo's writings remained banned until 1835; only then were they removed from the Index. From the mid-eighteenth century on, the new teachings were tacitly tolerated, and so they gradually ousted the old, false notions about our universe.

By reason of a quite special circumstance Galileo's discovery of the four Jupiter moons proved to be extremely useful. The orbital planes of the Jupiter moons happen to lie in almost the same plane as the orbit of Jupiter. This causes them to be *eclipsed*. From the times of these eclipses it is possible to determine with great accuracy the difference in longitude between the position of an observer and some other fixed point on the earth's surface. For this purpose it is necessary to know the time of a lunar eclipse in terms of some particular local time—for example, Amsterdam Mean Time. If the time of the same eclipse is then established in terms of the local time of the point one wishes to determine, the difference between these two times gives the required difference in longitude between the observation point and Amsterdam.

The value of this information to all seafaring peoples was very great. For a long time it was the sole basis of calculation used on ships. Then, sometime about 1675, the Danish astronomer Olaus Roemer found, by watching the Jupiter moons, that the eclipse times deduced from observation of these satellites fluctuated. When Jupiter was *in quadrature* with the sun, the times observed tallied pretty well.

When a star is in the same celestial longitude as the sun, the moon, or one of the planets, astronomers say it is *in conjunction* with the sun, the moon, or the planet in question. Where there is a difference of 180 degrees, they say the star is *in opposition* to the other heavenly body concerned. If the difference in celestial longitude is 90 degrees, the bodies are said to be *in quadrature* with each other.

Thus, the changing position of Jupiter referred to by Galileo and later by Roemer can be briefly described in this way: Jupiter reaches its minimum celestial-longitude value when in conjunction with the sun, its maximum when in opposition to the sun, and its mean longitude value when in quadrature with the sun. Roemer found that at periods when it was not in quadrature there was a time difference of up to 16.6 minutes. How did this come about? "The reason for the time difference," Roemer stated, "is to be found in the distance of Jupiter from the earth. This distance alters periodically during the revolution of the earth around the sun. When the earth is closest to Jupiter, the same eclipse is perceived 16.6 minutes earlier than when the two planets are at their greatest distance apart. Thus, during one revolution, the earth must pass through two points at which the time difference is only 8.3 minutes. However, the messenger that carries the news of the eclipse to us is light. In the one case, the light has a considerably longer distance to travel than in the other. In one case, it reaches the earth 16.6 minutes earlier and, in the other case, the same period later. It

follows that light has a finite and not, as was supposed
earlier, an infinite speed."

How could the speed of light be ascertained? To do this
it was necessary to know the width of the earth's orbit
around the sun. This problem was solved by the French
astronomer Jean Dominique Cassini, who calculated the required dimension after finding out the distance between the
earth and the sun. He arrived at a mean distance of around
93 million miles, and at a figure of about 186 million miles
for the diameter of the earth's orbit. During a single revolution around the sun, the earth twice touches a point at
which one and the same eclipse is seen with a time difference of 8.3 minutes, as compared with the time at the position where the earth is closest to Jupiter. If we divide the
diameter figure of 186 million by 16.6 minutes, we obtain a
speed of 186,000 miles per second.

In November 1675 Roemer submitted his work to the
French Academy of Sciences. All he achieved for his pains
was ridicule. The verdict of the "learned gentlemen" was
devastating: "It is absolutely impossible for anything, unless
it be the Spirit of God, to attain such a speed as that on
which the calculations of M. Roemer, the astronomer, are
based." Roemer's work was forgotten.

Fifteen years after his death the British astronomer
James Bradley started out from the same observations that
Roemer had made, and Bradley's thinking ultimately led to
a conclusive figure for the speed of light. Later, with more
precise measurements, this figure—186,000 miles per second
—was repeatedly arrived at.

Bewildering Vistas

A ray of light directed along the 25,000 miles of the
earth's equator would return to its starting point in 0.13
seconds. In one second it would have covered the distance

seven or eight times. By comparison, sound, which travels at only 1,086 feet per second, would require 33⅓ hours, while an express train with a speed of sixty miles per hour would need 17⅕ days, assuming its journey were unbroken.

Astronomers have made the speed of light the basis of a new system of measurement. Distances between the earth and individual stars are measured by the speed of light in a particular period of time—e.g., a second, a minute, or a year. This does not convey a period of time; what is meant is rather the distance covered by light in a second, a minute, or a year. For a second, we obtain the well-known figure of 186,000 miles, and for a year—a light year—roughly 5.880×10^{12} miles (one year = 31.5 million seconds). But how is the distance of stars from the earth determined?

The procedure adopted by astronomers for stars is the same as that used by surveyors in measuring the earth. It is based on the fundamental fact that all the parts of a triangle are known if one side and the angles are given. As early as the third century B.C. the Greek astronomer Aristarchus of Samos used this knowledge to work out a method of calculating the distance of the sun and the moon from the earth, as well as their size. He reasoned that when the sun illuminates exactly half of the moon, the line joining the eye of the observer on earth to the moon on the one hand and that joining the moon and the sun on the other must form an angle of 90 degrees. Once he had determined the angle formed by the line earth-moon with the line joining the earth and the sun, it was easy to work out the shape of the triangle that had the earth, the moon, and the sun as its corners. This also supplied the distances from the sun and the moon. Nevertheless, the moment at which exactly half the moon is lit up by the sun was difficult to gauge, and Aristarchus could only approximate it. The figures he obtained for the distances therefore differed considerably from the values known today. This was caused entirely by insufficient accuracy in measuring astronomical angles, the error in which at that time amounted to some ten minutes of arc.

Let us recall the circular protractor. It is divided up into 360 degrees, each of 60 minutes of arc, and each minute of arc into 60 seconds of arc. 10 minutes of arc represent an astronomical error of observation equivalent to one third of a full moon, an error that could lead to sizable miscalculations.

With Galileo's telescope the accuracy of astronomical observation increased to a tolerance of plus or minus 5 minutes of arc. By the middle of the eighteenth century this tolerance was no more than plus or minus 0.5 minutes of arc. With the standard telescopes of today we can achieve accuracy to within plus or minus 0.025 seconds of arc. This represents a degree of accuracy 1,000 times as great as that attained in the ancient world. By the use of the most modern telescope astronomical precision is carried much further— to plus or minus 0.01 seconds of arc; compared with observations in the ancient world, this means an increase in accuracy of 2,000 times. Viewed through the reflector lens used on Mount Palomar, the stars appear to us about 10,000 times more intense than they did through Galileo's telescope. A comparison has shown the reflecting telescope to be about a million times more sensitive than our eyes.

If the moon is looked at through a medium-size telescope, it is possible to distinguish objects 30 to 100 yards apart. We should therefore be able to recognize the layout of a "moon city" in all its details. With the same telescope the smallest perceptible objects on Venus would measure at least 7½ miles in any direction; smaller objects would merge into a dot. Two points on the surface of the sun would need to be at least 25 miles apart if they were to be detected as separate objects, and on Neptune—thirty times farther away—they would have to be 750 miles from each other. An object on Neptune, to be barely distinguishable with a medium-size telescope, would actually be as big as the moon. But what could we expect if we were to try to penetrate as far as the regions of the fixed stars? We should not encounter those nearest to the earth until we had traveled more than 300,000 times the distance to the sun. A dot on this fixed star would in reality be as big as our own sun.

The moon is roughly 238,000 miles from the earth, but through the 200-inch instrument on Mount Palomar it looks as close as if it were moving around the earth only 25 miles away. This would enable us to distinguish between two points no more than 15 to 50 feet apart. If we can make out the light of a candle with the naked eye for a distance of up to 6 miles, this means that by using the "Titan's eye" we could discern the candlelight at a distance of 6,000 miles or photograph it at 20,000 to 25,000 miles. Through this giant telescope a theatrical filament lamp burning on the moon would be visible without trouble on the night of a new moon.

The Mount Palomar telescope enables us to explore a region 50 billion times as large as that which we can take in with the naked eye. Although this instrument enables us to push forward some billion light years into the universe and peer into space with our vision magnified, as it were, a million times, we so far have access to a total of only a few billions of stars. Something like a billion times as many are still hidden from us. But the optical inadequacy of our astronomical giant is really made manifest to us only when we realize that the fixed stars—even those closest to us— do not appear to us one jot bigger through the telescope than when seen with the naked eye. They remain infinitesimal points of light of no diameter.

By the construction of this huge astronomical telescope, the world of Copernicus—that boldly conceived cosmos with its central sun and sister planets moving around it— has been reduced to an insignificant miniature colony of the universe; a universe in which not thousands or hundreds of thousands but billions upon billions of suns revolve in the same way as the one that brightens our day; a universe with space for more than two billion Milky Ways, many of which are vaster and more richly endowed with suns than the one immediately visible to us; a universe that even light, the swiftest messenger of nature, is able to traverse only in billions of years.

If we could accompany a light ray on its journey, we should experience a series of remarkable surprises. The Pole Star, for instance, is about fifty light years away from us. Thus, in the night sky we see light that left that star's surface fifty years ago. What would happen if we suddenly found ourselves transported to the Pole Star? We should be able actually to relive the events that took place on earth fifty years ago. So, if we were fifty years of age, we should see ourselves lying in the cradle again. We should once more go through our own first attempts to walk—everything, in fact, that lies fifty years back in time. The whole of the past would pass in review before our eyes. It would be as if the past were not past. But is it really past? Is the law of time and of the passage of time valid for the universe as well as for our earth?

Let us imagine ourselves sitting astride a beam of light and traveling with it. At the beginning of our journey let us fix a situation in our minds: the face, say, of a child in the act of smiling. Now we move, with this impression, away from the child at the speed of light. We are riding, as it were, at the tip of the beam of light which is to convey the face, and in the process the whole picture remains vividly before our eyes. The picture with which we are traveling is like a snapshot. The captured features of the child remain fixed and motionless, even when we move millions of years away from the child—which in the meantime has long since died. Have we, in the course of our "lightback" ride, suspended time? Have we preserved the present? A philosopher would put it something like this: "The farther we move away from an object we are observing, the closer we approach the past."

The picture presented by the earth when it was as yet "not formed and void" is still on the move, and an observer at a point, say, 50 million light years from the earth would see the earth precisely as it looked 50 million years ago. To him, this condition would represent reality. And if we were to transport ourselves a mere 5,000 light years from the earth, we should see the pyramids being built while in reality President Nasser was showing one of those mighty structures to visiting Marshal Tito. We should not really *experience* Nasser until about 5,000 years hence. What is happening at present on earth is still a remote prospect to the observer 5,000 light years away. If we now dissolve back to our own earth and focus the giant Mount Palomar telescope on a star 50 million light years away, we shall see that star as it looked 50 million years ago. In reality, the star may have vanished; it may have exploded long ago. If that explosion is to bring about the destruction of our own solar system, disaster is already on its way to us at the speed of light without our being aware of the fact.

But let us stay in the vicinity of the earth. To the observer on the Pole Star, from which we originally set out, World War I is still raging and Woodrow Wilson is still President of the United States.

The "Phantom" of Light

When Sir Isaac Newton recorded in his diary that a piece of polished glass in the shape of a prism enabled him to split up sunlight, he did not know that he was repeating what Leonardo da Vinci had noted down, in mirror writing, 200 years earlier.

One day, in the palace of Lodovico Sforza in Milan,

Leonardo covered the room allotted to him as a workshop from top to bottom with black paint. He then began covering the windows with black paper. Finally, he took a panel out of the heavily carved door and fastened a thick sheet of paper in its place. He now pierced this paper with a fine needle, and, as anticipated, sunbeams poured through the tiny hole into the darkened room. A cone of light fell across the room, forming a circle on the opposite wall.

Next he tried some tricks. When he held a white sheet of paper against the light rays some distance from the minute hole, it showed the outlines of the equestrian statue of Francesco Sforza standing in the sunlit piazza outside the door. True, the image was upside down, and it was not very sharp. But the moment he moved the white sheet nearer the small hole, the outline became sharper. In the end, the likeness was quite clearly recognizable in all its details. Leonardo thereupon fetched a bouquet of flowers and set it up outside the door. He wanted to see if the colors would show on the paper as well. They did show. As always, he wrote down his observations in his notebook. This time the entry ran: "If pictures of illuminated objects enter a very dark room through a small hole, let these pictures be intercepted inside the room on a piece of white paper, and it will be possible to observe all these objects on the paper in their true color and form."

In the course of his experiments Leonardo found something else. If he put a three-edged piece of glass in the path of the light rays, a pencil of colors appeared in place of the shining beam. The colors corresponded exactly to those which can be seen in a rainbow. Fearing that these experiments of his, particularly the last, might be regarded as "devil's work," he resolved to maintain rigid silence. He betrayed the secret only to his journal—in mirror writing.

The pencil of colors coming from the prism—for that was the instrument concerned—is always the same. The sequence of colors, too—Leonardo distinguished only five, not the seven we know today—always appears in the same order: red, orange, yellow, green, blue, indigo, and violet. This consistency of the phenomenon was enigmatic to early investigators, who named it "spectrum" and regarded it as a "phantom of light." They realized that not all light is the same; they saw that differences existed; and, above all, they noted the close connection between light and matter. Did not any body, when brought to radiant heat, give off its own specific light?

Georgius Agricola (1494–1555), the founder of petrology and the science of mining, went into the subject in detail. "It must be possible," he wrote, "to obtain from the color of a flame enlightenment concerning the materials burning therein." How did he come to make such an assertion? Like his contemporary, Paracelsus, he had discovered that in the dark a flame of pure alcohol changed color when the salts of certain metals were burned in it. The flame took on a yellow tinge as soon as a few grains of common salt were dropped into it. He therefore concluded that the coloration in question could be caused only by the common salt. We know today that it is the sodium in the salt which causes the yellow coloring. We further know that potassium salts, when burned, produce a violet color, strontium salts red, and barium salts green.

The first man to make a scientific study of flames colored in this way was the Scotsman Thomas Melvill in 1752. But he, too, was unable to supply answers to many questions. Not until a century later—in 1859—was knowledge far enough advanced to answer the most important of them. The credit for investigating the light of such flames more closely belongs to two Heidelberg professors: the physicist Gustav Robert Kirchhoff (1824–1887) and the chemist Robert Wilhelm Bunsen (1811–1899). At first they made use of a prism only. When the light of flames so colored was passed through a prism, sharply defined single lines in unmistakable colors appeared. To be able to observe these better, the two scientists constructed a simple but highly effective and sensitive instrument. The whole apparatus was rigged up from an empty cigar box, a prism, and parts of an old, disused telescope. It was the first *spectroscope*, a little thing on three legs like a microscope, and provided with an eye-slit. Inside it the light rays made their way through lenses and the prism. With this instrument it was possible to study the spectra of red-hot bodies and gases much more accurately than with a prism alone.

It became evident that red-hot bodies, melts, and gases each give off a quite characteristic individual light. The composition of the light from a candle flame, for example, turned out to be quite different from that of a gas flame, which in turn differed from sunlight. Whereas the spectrum of sunlight shows a continuous ribbon of colors (i.e., an unbroken succession), red-hot gases display a so-called *line spectrum*. Colored single lines appear, according to the kind of gas under inspection. In special circumstances they may merge into ribbons of light, but do not then show connecting links.

Until the middle of the last century identification of the elements had been the exclusive domain of chemists. But to identify a substance exactly, they had to have a quantity that could be weighed. Spectrum analysis now made it possible to identify a substance even when the quantity available "weighed" no more than one seventy-five-millionth of an ounce. Moreover, spectrum analysis virtually excluded any possibility of wrong identification. "The accuracy of spectrum analysis," Kirchhoff and Bunsen stated, "has its cause in the fundamental law of physics whereby the smallest particle of any substance, when brought to red heat, emits quite definite light waves of varying length, with the result that the spectra of two different elements never exactly coincide even in a single line. In practical terms, this means that whenever a spectrum shows a strong, single red line, it is known that the element burning in the flame is potassium. When, on the other hand, sodium is burned, two separated yellow lines appear. Burning hydrogen shows four lines: one red, one dark blue, and two violet."

There was no chance of confusion: each substance showed characteristics by which it could be clearly differentiated from every other. To the chemist the spectrum picture soon became what photographs or fingerprints are to the criminologist. This "dossier" made possible the discovery of a whole series of previously unknown elements. Bunsen, for instance, found two metals at once in Dürkheim mineral water. In one of them the operative line in the spectrum was blue-green (latin: *caesius*), in the other dark red (latin: *rubidus*). So he called the substance with the blue-green line *caesium* and the other *rubidium*. In the same way, François Lecoq de Boisbaudran discovered another element in zinc blende. As a good patriot, he called it *gallium* after his native land.

In the sludge of the lead chambers of a sulfur plant at Tilkerode in the Harz Mountains, William Crookes found the element *thallium*, which betrayed itself by a then unknown green line. The discoverer gave the new element this name because the greek word *thallos* means "green branch."

While examining zinc blende at Freiberg, Theodor Richter came upon a line that he found striking. He established that the element revealed in this way was *indium*, a substance not known until then. Indium has nothing to do with India; in naming the metal the discoverer was thinking of indigo, the color of the vital line in the spectrum of the new element.

In a similar manner, *scandium* was found by Lars Fredrik Nilson, *germanium* by Clemens Winkler, and *neon* by Sir William Ramsay.

No apparatus is so universally suited to all branches of

research as the spectroscope. With its help, the light of unidentified stars and of the sun can be investigated as thoroughly as that of a burning candle. It enables us to find out not only the weight of any particular star in the sky, but also whether the red glow of Mars harbors plant life. From chemists and physicists, work with the spectroscope has sometimes demanded the mental acuteness of a detective. Thus, it actually happened that one element was first discovered not on the earth, but on the sun. During the solar eclipse in 1868, Sir Norman Lockyer put his spectroscope to work to observe its colored sphere, the *chromosphere*. In the process he encountered a bright yellow line in the yellow-green sector of the spectrum. This was as yet unknown to scientists, and must therefore belong to a new element. Having made certain of this, they gave it the name *helium*, "that which pertains to the sun." Probably the first scientist to observe terrestrial helium was the American chemist W. F. Hillebrand, who in 1891 obtained an inert gas by heating uraninite; however, he failed to investigate the matter further. It was another four years before the gas was properly isolated. In 1895 the Englishman Sir William Ramsay was examining various rocks in search of argon, an element then rare. For this purpose he heated cleveite, a metal related to uranium pitchblende, until it was red hot, and focused his spectroscope on the luminous gases. There, to his astonishment, he found the same helium line. This provided the final proof that the "sun gas" is by no means confined to the sun, but is also to be found on the earth.

Dark Lines in the Spectrum

Spectrum analysis made it possible for still other questions to be answered—for example, the problem of the significance of the *dark lines* in the solar spectrum. These

lines had caught the attention of the Englishman William
Hyde Wollaston as early as 1802, but he did not pursue his
discovery further. About thirteen years later the lines were
rediscovered by the German physicist Joseph von Fraunhofer (1787–1826).

Starting as a glazier's apprentice, Fraunhofer had made
himself one of the most celebrated scholars of his time,
and ranked as an authority in the field of optics. Wollaston had found only two dark lines in the solar spectrum, the strongest. Fraunhofer, using glass lenses that he
ground himself according to a formula which he kept a
closely guarded secret, managed to detect no less than 600
such lines. These lines—later named *Fraunhofer lines*—
were always found in the same place, no matter what
prisms were employed. Strangely enough, they were absent
from the spectrum of artificial light. This was odd and not
immediately comprehensible. From the practical point of
view, the dark lines could only be due to the nature of
sunlight. Whether this explanation was the right one or not,
Fraunhofer himself did not know. The answer was finally
supplied by Kirchhoff and Bunsen. They established the
fact that these dark lines were so-called absorption lines.
They always occur when non-glowing gases are in the
presence of a glowing body. "Each individual dark line,"
the two scientists said, "is the result of a weakening or
absorption of light by cool, and therefore non-glowing,
gases in proximity to it. The things absorbing the colored
light in question are quite definite substances in the cool
mass of gas—substances, in fact, of the same nature as those
which would emit the colored light if they were in the red-
hot state. An orange-colored line which appears in the solar
spectrum can therefore only be absorbed by a substance
which, in the glowing state, would give rise to an orange-
colored line."

They thus provided for the first time a clear explanation
of the manner in which the solar spectrum is produced:

all light given off by the sun originates from substances
present in the sun. Each of these substances has its own
characteristic spectrum. All the individual spectra of the
various substances in the sun together form the rainbow
spectrum. If we were to withdraw one element after another from the solar sphere, removing each one in its
entirety, the spectral picture of sunlight would become
progressively simpler—that is, the lines appearing would be
come fewer and fewer. If we withdrew all the iron from
the sun, the solar spectrum would lose some 3,288 lines; the
elimination of titanium would take away around 1,085 lines;
the exclusion of chromium would cut out some 1,028, that
of nickel about 627; in the case of vanadium, there would
be some 618 lines fewer, and in the case of manganese
about 458 lines fewer. Now, if the masses of non-glowing
gas surrounding the sun contained one of these elements,
this element would absorb all the lines corresponding to its
own nature. If iron, for instance, were present in the non-
glowing gaseous belt, the iron lines would cease to appear
in the solar spectrum.

To prove this, Kirchhoff and Bunsen heated a piece of
chalk with an oxyhydrogen blowpipe until it was white
hot, and passed the brilliant light given off by the chalk
through the spectroscope. The spectrum, of course, at once
showed the familiar structure. This was all clear and not at
all surprising. The experiment became interesting when the
rays emitted by the chalk were passed through a low-temperature flame containing sodium before they reached the
spectroscope. Immediately a dark double line appeared in
the yellow sector of the spectrum at the very point where
a bright double line would normally be shown by that flame
if examined on its own. While the flame allowed all other
colors to pass through without hindrance, it intercepted
those rays of the light which had the same color as its own.
In fact, it intercepted more of these than were being
emitted by its own luminosity, owing to its low tempera-

ture. These missing lines appeared in the spectrum as *dark* spaces—that is, dark lines. These lines fill a gap, so to speak, and from its location conclusions can be drawn about the nature of the elements present in the sun. Up to now some 21,835 dark lines have been established in the solar spectrum alone. They are all meticulously recorded in the famous Rowland Photographic Map of the Normal Solar Spectrum.

A question that had always been intimately bound up with all these matters was the problem of the nature of light. Throughout his life Newton favored the atomistic conception. He visualized light as an extremely fine rain made up of tiny droplets. This, in his view, was emitted by every self-illuminating body. Newton had supporters, but far more opponents who rejected such a theory. One of these was Christian Huygens, who accounted for the processes of light as being similar to those of sound. According to him, light was caused by "longitudinal" vibrations of the "universal ether"—that is, vibrations occurring in the direction of propagation. He pictured these vibrations as being analogous to the waves set up on a smooth sheet of water into which a stone is thrown. He assumed that the bearer of these light waves was an ether of special consistency. This "ether" created confusion in people's minds at all times because nobody could visualize what it might be. The French physicist Augustin Jean Fresnel (1788–1827) defined it as a very thin, elastic substance filling space. Whereas the pitch of a sound depends on the wave length or frequency, color is the essential factor in light. Thus, Huygens stated, violet and blue light have the highest frequency and the shortest wave length; green and yellow light have a lower frequency and a longer wave length; while red light consists of the slowest vibrations and the longest waves. Sunlight contains all the waves shown by the spectrum. When light passes through a glass prism,

Huygens said, the light waves of varying length are refracted in varying degrees: violet most strongly, red least of all. All wave lengths combined form the colorless beam of light before refraction.

By the turn of the nineteenth century the English physician Thomas Young (1773–1829) had determined the wave lengths of the rays of visible light. Later, efforts were made to achieve more precise measurements. The longest wave in the visible range is 0.0008 millimeters, the shortest 0.0004 millimeters. If these figures are coupled with a velocity of propagation of 186,000 miles per second, the frequency (i.e., the vibration rate per second) is not difficult to calculate. Thus, a wave 0.0008 millimeters long vibrates 375,000 billion times per second about an equilibrium, and a wave 0.0004 millimeters long 750,000 billion times per second.

What do we mean by a wave? A wave that can propagate itself freely is equivalent to a steady succession of undulations, the crests of which are separated by a fixed distance. This distance between the crests is known as the *wave length*. The undulations move together in the direction of propagation at a fixed speed, which in the case of light is 186,000 miles per second. Many of the phenomena of light —though not all of them—could be explained in terms of the wave theory.

The Constant h: The Magic Key to Physics

During one of the last bombardments of Berlin in 1945 some teen-agers attached to an anti-aircraft unit and a few elderly members of the *Volkssturm* dragged a completely dazed, very old man out from under the ruins of a house. They carried him on a stretcher to a nearby shed, where he gradually recovered. Two years later this octogenarian— Max Planck—died, well-nigh forgotten, in dismal poverty.

In 1957 the Federal Republic struck a coin in his memory.

Max Planck's rise to the ranks of the great men of physics began with a lecture he gave on December 14, 1900, at a meeting of the Deutsche Physikalische Gesellschaft (German Society of Physicists) in Berlin. The core of this lecture was a new method of calculating the energy of rays. At the end of his observations Planck remarked that the existing laws of the theory of heat, based on the idea of a continuous exchange of energy and following from the wave theory of light, would not fit in with the results of the most recent measurements made at the Physikalisch-technische Reichsanstalt (Reich Institute of Physical Technology). On the contrary, he said, it must be assumed that heat and the energy in light do not flow continuously—i.e., steadily—but "in droplets," for which he coined the expression *quanta*.

How did Planck come to cast doubt on the "classical laws" of the physics of radiation? What led him to speak about quanta of light when it was already proved that all light had the character of waves? Planck first began to have doubts when he saw that values he had obtained experimentally could not be reconciled with the prevailing picture of classical physics. This applied particularly in the case of so-called *cavity radiation* or *black-body radiation*, the names applied to radiation given off by a hollow cylinder.

If one looks into a tube that has been blackened on the inside, the interior appears completely dark. In the language of the physicist, it is "absolutely black." Such a black body is described as having the property of absorbing all incoming radiation. If a black body—a platinum tube sealed at one end, let us say—is heated till it glows, we obtain a source of light that is ideal for measuring purposes. A black body's property of absorbing light of all wave lengths when immersed in radiation of higher temperature than its own is manifested as the property of emitting light of all wave

lengths when surrounded by radiation of lower temperature. Light rays coming from the interior walls of the
platinum tube and emerging through a narrow slit contain
all wave lengths and constitute the most perfect form of
radiation for measurement purposes so far known. It is
called cavity, or black-body, radiation because it comes
from the interior of a hollow metal body. It lacks none of
the specific colors, and all of them are present at full
strength. Black-body radiation started the line of thought
which caused Max Planck to question the "classical" theo-
ries of heat and light.

In his reasoning Planck set out from an ordinary natural
phenomenon. When we strike a tuning fork, it sets up
vibrations—i.e., it radiates sound. As we know, this sound
dies away after a while. If the tuning fork is not struck
again, it comes to rest in the same way as a wave on a
smooth water surface. This phenomenon had been scientifi-
cally proved, and was the subject of clear laws. But these
laws did not apply to black-body radiation. Under normal
conditions, the majority of the rays would have consisted
of ultraviolet light. In actual fact, however, the bulk of
them were in the red range—that is, at the very opposite
end of the spectrum. The black-body radiation had been
precisely measured with the aid of an extremely accurate
diffraction grating, a plane metal plate with fine parallel
slits. This procedure utilizes an effect by which light, when
it falls obliquely on a ruled grating—the parallel slits just
mentioned—is diffracted around the edge. The result is a
diffraction spectrum—that is, a succession of spectral lines
whose color gives exact information about the wave length
of the incoming light. The outcome of all these experiments
was always the same: where violet had been conjectured,
red appeared, and vice versa. Conclusions could be drawn
from this in regard to the energy given off by a radiant
body, but these conclusions did not fit in with contemporary notions; on the contrary, these notions were flatly

challenged by the measurements obtained. What was to be done? Planck saw only one way out: a radical departure from the classical laws of physics. This meant a revision of the laws according to which every change of state occurs "continuously"—that is, in an unbroken flow. "I find myself driven almost against my will," said Max Planck at the time, "to an assumption unsuspected up to now in physics: the electromagnetic energy emanating from the source of heat is not continuous, but is divided up, as it were, into definite portions or 'quanta.' Only if we concede such an assumption can we understand the spectral distribution associated with black-body radiation, a distribution that can be worked out with extreme accuracy."

In the mathematical evaluation of these strange results Planck came upon an inconceivably small figure to which a deeper significance seemed to attach. Within the formal framework of the radiation laws enunciated by Planck, this figure, calculated as 6.623×10^{-27} erg second, occupied the place of an invariable quantity. He called this quantity h.

On that evening, December 14, 1900, no one among those present could have suspected that the constant h ("Planck's elementary quantum of action") would become the greatest and most fruitful discovery of the century. What the mysterious quantity h was to mean to physics was rapidly demonstrated. It made its appearance wherever radiation phenomena were investigated. At first Planck himself was alarmed by his own discovery. For a long time he contested the view that his constant h had caused a revolution in classical physics, a science long since regarded as "terminated." When he recalled how his old teacher Philipp von Jolly had advised him not to take up physics because there was nothing more to be gained in this field unless one was "content to classify some particle or vesicle in this or that odd corner," his own assertions seemed to him almost like sacrilege. That was just how they appeared to many of his colleagues and former teachers. For a long time he was the object of violent criticism. He was even shunned and, more terrible still, passed over in silence. It was left to another "outsider," Albert Einstein, to draw the conclusions from Planck's discovery in 1907. He completed the revolution in the physicist's vision of the world, a task for which the "conservative Prussian" Planck, as the mathematician Hermann Weyl once put it, felt no urge.

The "elementary quantum of action"—the figure h—proved to be the magic key that was to open many doors previously closed.

Since heat and light are phenomena that are not confined to the dead aspects of nature but also play a considerable role among living organisms, the quantity h was soon to show itself inextricably bound up with all natural phenomena. Wherever a hand moved, an eye opened, or a foot stirred; in every movement affecting a molecule or an atom; wherever light was generated, and wherever the eye saw color and body: there the figure h was to be found invisible in the background.

In the years after 1900 Max Planck's life was devoted to work on the theoretical extension and experimental confirmation of his discovery. He was awarded the Nobel Prize for physics in 1918.

The results of his *quantum theory* compelled researchers more and more to shift the weight of their thinking from the domain of classical physics to the regions of microphysics. This involved an advance into the world of the infinitesimal particle, the world of the atom.

The Origin of Light

In 1943 a fifty-eight-year-old Danish scientist, threatened by arrest by the infamous Gestapo, fled from German-occupied Denmark and managed to reach the Swedish shore in a small motor craft. British friends having secured asylum for him in their country, he soon left Sweden in a British bomber. The pilot has been instructed to provide his passenger with a parachute and, in the event of an attack by enemy aircraft, to jettison him through the bomb bay. The fugitive, having no inkling of what might be in store for him, spent the whole flight lying on bomb doors that were liable to open at any moment. By mischance, none of the headsets that might have kept him in touch with the pilot fitted him when he tried them on. When the aircraft had climbed to a high altitude, he inevitably failed to hear the pilot's order to put on his oxygen mask. The pilot, on the other hand, believing that the passenger had understood his order, failed to realize that the man had been lying on the bomb doors unconscious for some time.

The fugitive who lived through this adventure was none other than Niels Bohr, the first man to reveal to us the architecture of the atom and the "miracle" of the origin of light.

27,000 billion atoms are mustered by nature to construct a cube of common salt with an edge length of one hundredth of a millimeter. All the beauty and simplicity of nature, with its inexhaustible array of forms and shapes, would unfold before the eyes of the man who managed to obtain a glimpse of this microcosmic world of the atom.

When the question of the origin of light was posed at the beginning of the twentieth century, relatively little was known about atoms. No one had so far encountered phenomena from which special data regarding the appearance of the atom could be deduced. Nevertheless, there was never any dearth of attempts to piece together a picture of its architecture from certain ideas. Among these various pictures, the interpretation given by Niels Bohr proved to be the most useful.

In December 1913 the scientist, then twenty-eight years

of age, delivered a lecture that was to inaugurate a new branch of physics. He pointed out at the very beginning of his talk: "We face the problem of unraveling the atom almost without aids. We are compelled to introduce new assumptions. In doing so, we have to see to it that these do not conflict with the facts of experience. To what extent this can be avoided on all points is something that time must show. The safest course would naturally be to make as few assumptions as possible."

The picture of the structure of the atom which he then outlined to his listeners was something like this. In all atoms a distinction is made between a shell, which houses particles of negative electricity, or electrons, and a nucleus. The electrical shell of the atom, made up of various skins as an onion is, encloses the tiny nucleus that carries a positive electric charge and practically determines the weight of a particular type of atom on its own.

"All rays, including light rays," Bohr stated, "have their origin in the atom. To induce an atom to emit light, however, we first have to convey energy to it. How does one supply an atom with energy? Various possibilities offer themselves. One way, for example, is to use heat. Sodium atoms, of which there are many trillions in a grain of salt, begin to glow as soon as they are heated in a candle flame. Others require a rather higher temperature to stimulate them to give off light. Another method of supplying energy to an atom is to expose it to an electric field, or to bombard it with electrons, or even to use light itself for this purpose.

"But what does an atom look like? The smallest and at the same time the lightest atom is that of hydrogen. This consists of an atomic nucleus and an electron that races around the nucleus at immense speed. However, definite orbits are allotted to the electron to which it normally adheres strictly and which it cannot leave under its own power."

Bohr then broached the problem of the formation of

light inside the atom. "As you may imagine," he said, "the discovery of the beautiful and simple laws governing spectra has given rise to many attempts to find a theoretical explanation for them. All these attempts were bound to fail because they were based on facts previously regarded as certain in the light of accepted natural laws. I have reason to assume that an atom cannot give off light outwards as long as the electrons in the shell of the atom revolve in their stationary orbits. If we keep in mind the fact that light is a form of energy, and that the emission of light by an atom is therefore always associated with a loss of energy that has to be compensated for in one way or another, it becomes clear that, in a system in which the objects capable of oscillating—the electrons—are kept at a constant energy level, energy—in our case, light—cannot possibly be given off outwards."

The atom does not indiscriminately accept energy conveyed to it. Its behavior is comparable to that of a slot machine that takes a variety of coins, with different slots for different coins. The slot for a package worth a quarter will only take quarters, and the slot for dimes will only take dimes. Just as a package worth a quarter cannot be obtained with a dime, so the electron shell of the atom will not accept energy that is not suitable.

The atom is thus very fastidious. It absorbs only energy that corresponds to "its nature." The sodium atom, for example, absorbs only an amount of energy roughly equivalent to that of a ray of yellow light. The potassium atom will always show preference for a quantity of energy equivalent to red light. The hydrogen atom will take in quantities of energy that correspond to the energy value of a ray of blue, red, or violet light.

Whenever an atom receives energy appropriate to its nature, the electrons in the shells are raised into a new "permitted" orbit, but they stay there only a very short time. For the most part, after about one hundred-millionth of a second, they jump back into their original orbit. While they are falling back into the old track, the energy that lifted them into the new path is released again. This is the energy that becomes visible as an electromagnetic wave and therefore as a ray of light. "The color of the light emitted," Bohr went on, "can be easily worked out by means of a very simple formula that was enunciated by Johann Jakob Balmer."

The Balmer Lines

In 1885 Balmer, a mathematician and physicist at Basle, Switzerland, was engaged in research on the spectrum of hydrogen, which consists of four lines. In the course of his studies he discovered that a curious connection exists between the various wave lengths of light waves, and that the connection can be reduced to a simple formula. On the basis of this formula Balmer was able to prove that, in addition to the visible lines in the spectrum of hydrogen, other, invisible lines—he calculated a total of thirty—must exist. All these lines were actually discovered in the course of time, and although in Balmer's day nothing had been known about electron orbits or atomic nuclei and shells, it now became possible to put the Balmer formula to excellent use in calculating electron orbits. Thus, in the case of the tiniest possible permitted "stationary" electron orbit in the hydrogen atom, it gave a radius of about 0.5 ten-millionths of a millimeter. For the second permitted path a radius of two ten-millionths was calculated, for the third four ten-millionths, and for the fourth eight ten-millionths of a millimeter.

To begin with, Bohr's model atom made possible an explanation of the four visible lines in the hydrogen spectrum. According to this, the red line appears when the single available electron is raised from its innermost orbit, the stationary orbit, to the third possible path, and from there drops back into the second possible orbit. If the electron jumps from the fourth orbit to the second, the hydrogen atom gives off a blue light. In the event of a jump from the fifth or sixth orbit to the second, the two violet lines appear. If, however, the electron reverts from the fifth or sixth orbit to the innermost, stationary, track, lines appear which are beyond the scope of our direct vision. These lines correspond to "dark" light that is invisible to us. As this kind of light appears in the spectrum next to the visible violet light, it was named *ultraviolet light* (ultra = beyond). If, however, the electron jumps back from one of the outer orbits to the third orbit near the nucleus, other lines appear which are not visible to our eyes. Here we are concerned with *infrared rays* having longer wave lengths—that is, again with "dark" light that we experience as heat. All light —indeed, all radiation—has its beginning in the atom, just as the atom in its turn becomes the receiving station for a great diversity of rays. "And as regards the 'miracle of light,' which comprises not only the visible light rays but also the invisible electromagnetic waves of the longer and shorter wave ranges," Niels Bohr said on one occasion, "they all have their true origin in constant transitions between their tracks, which are themselves fixed and immutable. But as to the true nature of light over and above that, I am unfortunately not in a position to supply the answer."

Rays Are Not Colors

Where there is no light, there is no color. The color of a body does not exist. It arises from the destruction of light in matter. How are we to understand this? Is the golden color of gold not real, not genuine? We speak of golden yellow, of copper red, of lavender blue, of grass green, of lemon yellow, steel blue, or silvery white, and we do so with a quite definite picture in our minds. Is it the atoms of gold or the copper or the silver atoms that give these metals their colors? By no means! The interior of gold or of copper or of silver is not golden, red, or silver in color. The atoms do not have any of these colors. The interior of things is dark, and where there is darkness there is no color. Color is conveyed to us by light. A body that is not itself radiant acquires its color only when countless atoms are massed and marshaled in the presence of light. Their order and grouping in crystals and molecules, their distance from one another, and the number of their layers, together with the kind of light, determine the color tone.

Color is the *dress* in which objects display themselves to us. This dress is an expression of light and of the inner order of molecules and atoms. Color is therefore nothing fixed or constant, nothing lasting or eternal. Let a certain amount of light energy be suppressed here, or the order of molecules and atoms within a substance be disturbed there, and at once the color of the object appears changed.

All physical colors that man registers and on the strength of which he distinguishes one thing from another are related to sunlight. Physical colors are therefore not realities. They are based on familiarity and are consequently merely thought-habits. However, the thought-accustomed color at once becomes unaccustomed when we observe the object in light other than that of the sun. That is something any cloth merchant knows. A material in artificial light looks quite different from the same material in daylight. How does this come about? The atoms and molecules in things are arranged in meaningful order. In rock salt, for instance, chlorine and sodium atoms alternate at the corners of little cubes lined up in rows. In other substances the order is quite different. Consequently, the behavior of substances toward light falling upon them is also variable. Only certain wave lengths of a light ray are absorbed; others pass through or are turned back. Therefore, only some of the light waves of varying lengths have a key that fits the many gates and gaps within substances. Now, among materials there are downright light-gluttons or light-guzzlers. They soak up light in much the same way as a dry sponge soaks up water. In such cases, not a glimmer of the incoming light is sent back. But where light is absent, darkness prevails; and so a body that "devours" all light has the effect of being black.

Lampblack, for example, behaves toward light rays in this way. Where a substance such as thin glass allows practically all light to pass through it with only nominal loss, the substance appears colorless and transparent. Such substances turn up their noses at light, but a large proportion of substances behave otherwise. Their atoms absorb only a proportion of the light. The remainder is sent back. Such substances or bodies appear to us to be colored. This physical color consists of a mixture of different wave lengths. In the case of copper, for example, the atoms absorb pretty well all the green, blue, and violet rays from the incoming beam of invisible light. The rejected remainder produces an over-all impression of a copper shade. It is not evident from the reddish effect of this color that it is, in fact, composed of a mixture of many individual lines in the residual spectral picture. In other words, light falling on atoms of matter loses quantities of energy corresponding to the spectrum lines of the elements in question. What we see is always only the color whose energy value has not been destroyed by the atoms in a body; and we consequently never see a color whose energy has been swallowed or absorbed.

We can convince ourselves of this by means of a small mental experiment. Let us assume that a sieve is the crystal lattice, and let the beam of light be represented by colored balls of different sizes, all those of the same color being the same size. Suppose, then, our sieve lets all the balls fall through except the red ones. We therefore see nothing but a uniform red surface. If, however, the red, yellow, and green balls fall through while the blue and violet balls do not, the surface looks to us from some distance like a mixed color, with the blue components clearly dominant.

The stricter the arrangement of atoms in bodies, the more firmly they are kept in place, the more precise their formation and the cohesion among them: the purer and more limpid the colors we perceive will be. These are the qualities we find in the crystals of precious stones. In the case of rubies, all the colors in sunlight are destroyed except the red ones; in emeralds, all except green; in citrines, all but yellow. All these have atoms that absorb part of the energy in a ray of sunlight and reject the rest. In emeralds, the green components of sunlight are barred by the presence of chromium atoms in the crystal lattice; in rubies, the red ones are blocked by a built-in iron oxide.

The slightest changes among the atoms within a molecular structure, the omission or addition of one type of atom or another, can turn a brilliant red into blue. We thus gain a glimpse of two worlds that will always mysteriously confront each other: on the outside, detached from man's sight and feeling, a frenzied dervish dance of electrons in the shells of atoms, a swirling and weaving of atoms in matter, an eternal back and forth of attraction and repulsion, a constant interchange of tiny forces, all ruled by the cold laws of number, ordered and determined by size, mass, position, and strength; and within ourselves, the other world, the world of colors, of tones, of perception in all its richness. Here, too, man strives to be the master of both worlds: wherever fancy turns or longing reaches, there is a conflict between the world of mind and the world of matter, between the way things seem and the way things are.

Our eye is twice a mirrow: a mirror of the soul and a mirror of a whole world of rays. Not until things have been viewed by our eyes do the processes and phenomena of nature acquire the clarity that lifts them out of the world of tangible reality into the world of the spirit.

It is the eye that transports us from the profound darkness that shrouds us all our days to the splendor of a world ablaze with color. Yet neither the red of the loveliest rose nor the green of the most superb emerald, neither the deepest blue of the heavens nor the purity of the seven colors displayed to us by the spectrum of the sun should obscure from us the fact that the eye lives surrounded by utter darkness. For the eye there are no reds, no greens, no violets, no yellows, no blues: there are only invisible light quanta containing varying amounts of energy, all of them minute. They race through the vitreous, jelly-like fluid in the eyes, leaving behind them on the retina an *impression*.

Nevertheless, the best eye on its own would be powerless if it did not hold the ends of innumerable nerve fibers that pick up the stimuli set up by the light quanta. Even these nerve fibers are ignorant of color and light. They know only chemical reactions, metabolic processes, and tiny electric currents. Again, the many millions of nerve fibers would be virtually superfluous if there were not certain areas in the brain specially designed to respond to the chemical and electrical reactions of these fibers. It is here that the impression produced by the photons—the light particles—on the light-sensitive layer of the eye first becomes *light* and *color*. The light we supposedly see with our eyes is not born in this layer nor in the nerve fibers. It first comes into existence in the brain. Light and color are therefore not outside us: we carry them within ourselves, for the world around us is blacker than the most stygian night.

The Two Faces of Light

The human mind recoils at the idea of imagining a "thing" that occupies no space, because experience teaches us that nothing exists which does not take up room. For light, however, the essential condition of existence does not lie in filling space, but rather in the fact of its being incessantly propagated in space at a constant and unexceeded speed. When light stops spreading through space, it stops being *light*. It ceases to exist. The same property is shown by sound. Sound, too, is audible only as long as it is propagated in water, in solid bodies, or in the air. In the case of sound, we know the medium that carries it. When we utter a cry, the molecules of the air begin to vibrate in a quite definite rhythm. In the process, one molecule bumps into another and transmits the vibration. If there were no molecules, as is the case in an airless vacuum, we could stand beside the most powerful aircraft engine without being disturbed in any way by the engine noise, which normally lies far beyond what is called the threshold of pain of our hearing.

But in what medium do light rays move? Like all electromagnetic rays, they are not bound to air or water or any other medium that can be explained. If they were so bound, light from a heavenly body could not reach us through space that is assumed to be empty. That is why it is so difficult for us to form a conception of light and of the other electromagnetic rays known to us. But even if we are not given the faculty of imagining light, we can at least comprehend its manifestations and pin them down with the aid of higher mathematics. This is the only science that helps man to penetrate into regions outside the scope of his imagination.

The physicist Augustin Fresnel put forward the theory of a "fundamental ether." In this, as he believed, light could be propagated in the form of waves. Today we know that light cannot be propagated in it for the simple reason that there is no such ether. In the modern view, it is only a mathematical fiction with no existence in reality.

When light and matter encounter each other, a curious transformation takes place. Light gives up its wave character and behaves like a tiny projectile. It turns out to have materialized. This means that a thing that could not be handled or weighed suddenly turns into something with physical properties. To prove this, we bombard an insulated metal plate with very fast electrons. It can be shown that some of the electrons penetrate the shells of individual atoms. What the electrons now experience is what happens to a projectile, for example, which is fired at strong armor plate: the electrons are sharply braked. They lose their kinetic energy with almost abrupt suddenness. After this sudden deceleration, the energy that previously propelled the electrons is absorbed by the atoms in the metal plate. The result is to make the electrons jump about inside their atom shells in a manner now familiar to us. But when electrons begin to jump about in the shells of atoms, light is produced. The energy of this light roughly corresponds to the kinetic energy of the electrons checked in their course. Surprisingly enough, this experiment can also be reversed. From this we realize that light behaves in the same way as bursts of small projectiles. To demonstrate this, we now expose an insulated upright metal plate to light of a very short wave length. Very soon the plate will show an electric charge. This, in turn, means that the light rays behave like little billiard balls. What they have done, in effect, is to punch electrons out of the shells of the atoms.

The birth of a light ray may be preceded by yet another strange process. This takes place, for instance, when a particle with the mass of the electron, but carrying a positive electric charge (such particles are called positrons), collides with an electron. As the two particles have the same weight, they should behave like two colliding billiard balls. In fact, they react quite differently. As one of the particles carries a positive charge and the other a negative charge, and as the charges are equal, they cancel each other out on contact. The masses vanish. They no longer exist. Their place is taken by electromagnetic radiation of a very short wave length. The strange thing about this is its energy content. It corresponds exactly to the energy content of the mass of an electron and a positron.

The reverse process has an air of magic about it. If a very short-wave electromagnetic ray reaches an atomic nucleus, the ray may suddenly vanish and take on material shape. It produces two particles of mass which we recognize as an electron and a positron. In nature, such processes are going on continually. Electromagnetic radiation, the Janus with two faces, reveals only one of them at a time. One shows us the form of a wave, the other a particle. Which of these is the true face is a question that cannot be answered. Presumably, light is neither a wave process nor is it made up of particles. To escape from this dilemma, a witty physicist has defined the nature of light as that of a "wavicle." At all events, light remains even now one of the greatest mysteries of nature. Whether or not a key to it is found in future will depend on the extent to which man can perfect his intellectual powers. At their present stage of development, our minds are like a house with five tiny windows. We can go to any one of them to see what is happening outside, but we cannot lean out. We have to be content with whatever chance may place outside one of the windows—and even then it remains open to question whether we immediately grasp what is presented to our gaze.

CHAPTER 2

"Sorcery"
with Infrared Rays

MAN IS PRE-EMINENTLY an optical creature. He owes between seventy and eighty per cent of his knowledge of the world around him to his eyes and to the quality of their vision. The eye performs incredible feats. Its little elastic lens, for example, undergoes between 4,000 and 6,000 changes in a day. It throws images of great clarity on the retina.

A piece of retina no bigger in area than the tip of a match contains about a million cells. None of these cells ever captures more than one light-impression at a time. This means that an object which makes a picture on our retina of about four square millimeters in size is in reality seen broken down into a million picture dots. Photographic plates and film work on the same principle: tiny specks, light-sensitive grains of silver bromide, are distributed in great numbers over the photographic layer. These, when exposed to light, are darkened in varying degrees and, when developed, together produce a picture.

The strangest thing about the structure of the retina is the position of the rods and cones—light-sensitive sensory cells. They are not, as one might imagine, turned toward the light, but away from it. First come the nerve fibers on the front surface of the retina. Then follow the layers of the nerve cells. Then, and only then, come the vision cells. Thus, before light reaches the vision cells, it has to pass through all the layers of the retina. This paradoxical arrangement of the elements of the retina goes back to the primeval days of life on earth when the light-sensitive sensory cells required appreciably stronger protection against light than they need today. As the structure of our eyes reveals, they have remained shielded from direct contact with light rays.

We use the term "light rays." Well, it is true that we live in a virtually boundless ocean of rays, a large proportion of which is made up of light rays. Of these, our eyes pick up only a minute fraction: the narrow band of visible light. An imaginative writer once maintained that our eyes would not be perfect until they could receive all the light rays that exist. That is a very bold contention indeed. If we were condemned to respond to all the rays that shower down upon us, our lives would become one long hell. There would be the radio waves of varying lengths that are incessantly sent out into space by innumerable radio stations; the waves we ourselves and our fellow human beings constantly give off in the form of heat; to these would be added the impenetrable rain of waves produced by cosmic radiation which make their way to us from some far corner or other of the universe; and piled on these would be the gamma rays of radioactive elements, X rays, ultraviolet rays and, not least, infrared and ultrared rays of all gradations. It is truly a blessing that we can apprehend only a minute segment of that gamut of waves with our eyes, just enough to enable us to relish the beauty of nature's multicolored palette.

Our retina is receptive to a quite definite range of electro-magnetic waves only. Furthermore, the degree of sensitivity fluctuates with the color value of the light. Red light stimulates the retina relatively little. The action of a ray of yellow light on the instruments of our vision is 28,000 times as intense as that of a red ray of equal strength; that of a greenish-yellow ray is 100,000 times more intense. The stimulus from violet light is some 10,000 times that of equally strong red light. If we look at these figures, we see that our eyes are most sensitive to yellow-green light. Maximum light-sensitivity is associated with a wave length of 0.00055 millimeters. As the wave length increases or decreases, the sensitivity of the eyes drops away to zero. The limit of vision is found at about 0.0008 millimeters, toward the end of the light spectrum where the long wave lengths lie. Beyond this point our eyes are plunged in darkness. The impression made on our eyes by the light here is so weak that no stimulation takes place.

Light of a wave length greater than 0.0008 millimeters falls in the range of the *infrared rays*. We experience these rays as heat. The longer such heat rays are, the more insensitive to them our eyes become. For instance, the sensitivity of our eyes to infrared rays with a wave length of approximately 0.00098 millimeters is no more than one fourteen-billionth part of their sensitivity to yellow light of equal strength. By way of contrast, the lowest energy density to which our eyes still show a faint reaction in yellow-green light stands at 0.00000046 watts per square centimeter. To achieve the same effect for a wave length of 0.00098 millimeters, we should have to use 6,500 watts per square centimeter. A firefly at a distance of twenty yards or more, where its light can still just stimulate our eyes, would have to be replaced by a giant searchlight. Even then, after our eyes had slowly become accustomed to the darkness, its beam would appear to us as a not so very dark speck against a black background.

We know of no living creature that would apprehend heat as light, but none would fail to respond emotionally to heat. Without heat, there is no life; and the effects of the phenomenon we call heat are immensely varied.

If we filter a sunbeam in such a way that all the visible rays are retained while the invisible infrared rays are allowed to pass through, and if we then place some guncotton at the focal point of these rays, it immediately explodes and goes up in smoke. Under the same treatment, paper bursts into flames, and magnesium wire begins to glow. A diamond splinter, placed for purposes of experiment in a flask of oxygen and then exposed to these unearthly rays, begins to glow like a star and finally burns away without residue. All this happens while the air at the focal point of the rays remains as cold as it is anywhere else in the room.

Even more remarkable things occur if we now place screens in the path of the rays of the same sunbeam— screens that allow the passage of only blue and violet light rays. If we direct the filtered rays at a twig coated with fine hoarfrost, we shall find it impossible to melt the covering. Even a snowflake put in the path of the rays on a well-cooled glass plate will not turn into water. Thus, the heat effect is produced only by the invisible infrared rays. We see this phenomenon demonstrated afresh every winter. When the snow on the ground melts one fine, sunny day, it melts not from the top down but from the ground up. Therefore, it is not the sun but the infrared heat rays given off by the earth that liberate us in the spring from the burden of the snow blanket. If the circumstances were reversed, the consequences would be incalculable. Water from the snow heaps melted during the day would flood huge areas, and these would then freeze over at night. As things are, the water from the snow melted from the ground up can flow away, and the snow cover bears down after it and slowly but steadily disappears.

There is a close relationship between the infrared rays and visible light. In contrast to visible light rays, infrared rays have longer wave lengths. They range from the darkest, barely visible red rays (0.0007 millimeters) to the shortest radio waves, which lie approximately between 0.4 and 0.5 millimeters. The infrared area most thoroughly investigated by the physicists covers the range from 0.0007 to 0.025 millimeters. The next band, about which very little is known, occupies the range from 0.025 to 0.02 millimeters. The adjoining band from 0.2 to 0.4 millimeters is virtually unexplored.

Infrared rays, like ordinary light, are observed by means of a prism, but it cannot be a prism of ordinary glass because ordinary glass swallows up a large proportion of the infrared rays. Accordingly, for investigation of wave lengths of up to 0.003 millimeters a quartz-glass prism is used. For wave lengths of up to 0.009 millimeters, we use fluorspar; for those of up to 0.014 millimeters, a rock-salt prism. For even longer infrared rays, such as those of up to 0.021 millimeters, a prism made of sylvite is required, and for rays of up to 0.031 millimeters, one of potassium iodide. Where the latter wave length is concerned, good results are also obtained with sensitive heat indicators, such as photoelectric cells with a lead-sulfide coating.

When a body is heated to a temperature of approximately 6,000 degrees centigrade (roughly 11,000 Fahrenheit), rays with wave lengths of 0.000200 to approximately 0.4 millimeters are emitted. A modern metal-filament lamp, with a filament heated to about 2,600 degrees centigrade (approximately 4,700 Fahrenheit), gives off infrared rays that for the most part have wave lengths of between 0.000700 and 0.001400 millimeters. The proportion of infrared rays compared with visible light is ninety-seven per cent; in the case of iron brought to white heat, it is as much as ninety-nine per cent.

What Is Heat?

Electrons dance in atoms, atoms in molecules, and molecules in space. When the temperature rises, their motion becomes livelier. What is it that drives molecules? What is it that imparts to them a speed of 300 miles per second and more? How do they move about in space? Do they move in straight lines or in curves? How far do they get? What is the temperature of a molecule? Do molecules have a temperature at all?

Let us imagine a hollow glass ball. If we could observe the molecules it contains, we should see them whirling around in all directions. This wild dance of trillions and trillions of minute billiard balls, as we may picture the molecules to be, can be whipped up to a frenzy if we turn infrared light on their glass prison for a moment. If we hold a thermometer in the vessel, we see the mercury column slowly rise. Were we to continue the heating process, a moment would come when the glass wall would burst. In the normal course of events we should not waste another thought on this everyday occurrence. We know, of course, that in this case the internal pressure is greater than the external pressure. But how many people stop to think that the greater part of our power technology is based on the process we have described? That it all starts with a more or less powerful movement of molecules?

The individual molecule is not "hot" or "cold." It has no temperature. What we call heat, or experience as heat, is nothing more than the uncontrolled movement of a multitude of molecules. In the realm of microcosmic matter, heat and movement are synonymous. To move a free molecule such as appears in gases, energy is necessary. But how do we impart energy to a molecule? One way consists in heating the gas. The molecule is not made warmer than it was before by this treatment, but it gains kinetic energy. In other words, it is accelerated. Now, owing to the myriads of molecules in a gas, a great many of them will come into collision. According to the density of the gas, the number of these collisions may run into billions or trillions or more. It may be noted, too, that under ordinary temperature conditions molecules move at a speed of about a mile per second. All the same, a molecule like this does not get very far before it cannons into another molecule and rebounds. This collision does not produce heat. Even if two molecules collide at great speed after a short journey, heat energy is neither gained nor destroyed. The collision merely causes an exchange of kinetic energy. Let us say, for example, that before the collision one of the molecules has 8 units of kinetic energy, the other 12. After the collision the proportions will perhaps be 10 to 10, or 5 to 15, or 3 to 17, or any other combination of figures that produces a total of 20. We see from this that the total amount of energy associated with molecules can be neither reduced nor increased, nor can it be otherwise transformed. It remains motion. Therefore, only faster movement of the molecules will cause the thermometer to rise, or arouse in us a stronger sensation of warmth.

The human body constitutes a self-regulating source of infrared heat. In summer and winter, whether under the blazing sun of the Sahara or in the icy wastes of Greenland, it maintains a constant temperature, apart from trivial fluctuations. The temperature remains at 98.6 degrees Fahrenheit, regardless of whether the body is well nourished or hungry. Of course, the body cells, the sources of our physical warmth, announce their demands for sustenance to the body in forceful terms. But they will go on working, for days if need be, without food, without fuel. In that event the body at once mobilizes its reserves. First it uses up its fat stocks—that is, it eats into its own tissue.

This dissipation of the body's own fat may reduce it to skin and bones, but its heating mechanism is left intact. The body temperature is maintained.

Nevertheless, there is one condition that may spell doom to the body, particularly if it is hungry: too drastic cooling down. To protect the body against this, the human skin possesses a number of special sensory cells. For protection against cold, there are cold-sensitive cells; for protection against heat, heat-sensitive points: a total of about 30,000 heat-sensitive points and about 250,000 cold-sensitive points, distributed all over the body. When the skin is cool, the *cold-receivers* react. They do so by transmitting nervous impulses to the mid-brain. From there, immediate contraction of the skin vessels and cold shivers are ordered. The signals consist of electrical impulses of a few millionths of a volt. Recently they were tapped and amplified sufficiently to make the cold shivers audible in a loudspeaker. But our sense of temperature has special peculiarities: the greater the density of a body we touch and the greater the number of heat and cold points excited by it, the more marked our sensation of temperature will be. Accordingly, the temperature being equal, a solid body will feel cooler to us than a liquid, and a liquid will feel cooler than a gas. Therefore, as far as feeling is concerned, a thermometer can no longer serve us as a yardstick.

To our bodies everything is cold that withdraws heat from them. Conversely, anything that conveys heat to them feels warm. A man bathing at 68 degrees Fahrenheit cools down to the same extent as if he went for a walk naked in the air at 32 degrees Fahrenheit, a temperature at which water becomes covered with a sheet of ice. A sheet of iron at 68 degrees Fahrenheit feels cold to us, whereas a piece of wood at the same temperature feels appreciably warmer. Yet an external temperature of 68 degrees gives us no sensation at all.

Iron is a good conductor of heat. It immediately draws

heat from the body—that is, contact with heat whips up the molecules of iron to greater mobility. The heat absorbed is at once transmitted from molecule to molecule. Wood, on the other hand, is a bad conductor of heat, and the heat that it draws from the body is carried from molecule to molecule with corresponding slowness. Air has an even lower heat-conductivity. In the case of iron a vast number of molecules immediately take part in the process of reception and transmission; with wood the number is considerably fewer, and with air fewer still, the temperature in all three instances being constant.

In a room in Seattle the velocity of air molecules at about a mile per second corresponds to a room temperature of approximately 68 degrees Fahrenheit. On the Glacier Peak the same temperature would appear to us appreciably warmer. This would not be because the velocity of molecules at that height is greater, but because the air is thinner and consequently takes considerably less heat from the body. At a height of 6,500 feet, cooling is already one third less than at sea level. This, and not intensive exposure to sunlight, is the reason why we need only light clothing for winter sports at high altitudes. *Cold* and *hot* are sensations. In nature there is no such thing as *cold:* there is nothing but a rise or fall in molecular motion. The molecules whirl in their frantic devil's dance or, in the extreme case, mark time. But *cold*—absolute molecular repose— does not exist.

Close to Absolute Zero [1]

Attempts to put heavy curbs on the movement of molecules first began to look promising in 1908 when the

[1] For scientific purposes, temperatures approaching absolute zero are generally given in the Kelvin scale of temperatures (named after its proposer, the British mathematician and physicist Lord Kelvin). There would be little point in converting, here, the centigrade figures into Fahrenheit. (Translator's note)

Dutch physicist Heike Kamerlingh Onnes, founder of the low-temperature laboratory that bears his name at Leiden in Holland, was able to liquefy hydrogen and helium. He based his approach on the formula for the liquefaction of gases worked out by the German engineer Karl von Linde. Briefly stated, this process, the model for all refrigerating machines today, consists in compressing gas in a coiled pipe. In practical terms, this means that the distance covered by the individual gas molecules is artificially restricted. The molecules now collide more frequently than before; they also hammer more often against the walls of their metal prison. When collisions between the molecules occur—several billion times per second—energy is exchanged. The faster molecule gives up part of its kinetic energy to the slower. The compressed gas is then allowed to expand suddenly. The result is a drop in temperature, caused by the fact that the distance traveled by the molecules has been artificially increased. Collisions between the individual molecules are no longer so frequent as before.

What has happened may be compared to an attempt to spread a drop of perfume about a room. We have to atomize the drop, to break it up into many, many billions of tiny droplets so that they are distributed uniformly through the room. Heat spreads in exactly the same way: what was previously a thimbleful of hot gas suddenly becomes a cubic yard of cold gas. The refrigeration process is accordingly a quite simple one: compression and sudden expansion of gases. The temperature rises in one case and falls in the other. In all experiments with liquefaction, one cooled substance is played off against another—that is, one helps to lower the temperature of the other still further. Brine is used to liquefy carbon dioxide (carbonic acid), then air is liquified with the carbon dioxide. Liquid air helps to convert hydrogen from the gaseous to the liquid state, and hydrogen in turn enters the cycle to cool helium to the point at which the gas becomes liquid. In 1913 Kamerlingh

Onnes was awarded the Nobel Prize for physics for this achievement. In 1922 he succeeded with liquid helium in getting within 0.83 degrees of absolute zero, which is at minus 273 degrees centigrade.

Gases can be liquefied by cooling them until they condense. Before this happens, the gas in question in transformed into a state known as *boiling*. The temperature at which this occurs is called the *boiling point*. It is always dependent on external pressure. For instance, water at a pressure of about two atmospheres (corresponding to 1,500 millimeters of mercury pressure) boils at 119 degrees centigrade. At a high altitude and a pressure that pushes the mercury column no higher than 526 millimeters, water boils at 90 degrees centigrade. A liquid can be forced to boil at lower pressure if the vapor that forms rapidly during boiling is pumped off. Using this method at Leiden in 1932, the Dutch scientist Willem Hendrik Keesom was able to achieve a mercury pressure of 0.036 millimeters. He thus came within 0.71 degrees of absolute zero.

For the attainment of even lower temperatures, other approaches had to be tried. In this context, a theory of the French physicist Paul Langevin was recalled, according to which deeper cooling can be secured by sudden demagnetization of magnetic materials. The first researcher who attempted to exploit this idea was the Dutchman Peter Debye. He began by cooling certain metal salts with liquid helium, and then subjected them to shock demagnetization. By this method a further drop in temperature was obtained. In 1935 at the Leiden low-temperature laboratory Wander Johannes de Haas and his colleagues, using the same principle with caesium-titanium-alum, reached a temperature of 0.0045 degrees above absolute zero. They used a giant electromagnet through which they put a 560-ampere current. In 1947 at Berkeley, California, Professor William Francis Giauque and Dr. Duncan P. MacDougall got down to a temperature of 0.0015 degrees above absolute zero. Giauque was awarded a Nobel Prize for chemistry in 1949 for his services to low-temperature research. Today the record stands at 0.0011 degrees above absolute zero. We have approached within one nine-hundredth of a degree of our goal.

One might now suppose that it can only be a matter of time before the state of absolute molecular repose is achieved. This is a mistake. For the lower we progress on a temperature scale, the more difficult it becomes to reduce the temperature still further. In fact, the difficulty increases on a logarithmic basis. It thus begins to become clear even to the greatest optimist that, while a closer approach to absolute zero may be possible, the likelihood of our reaching it by any finite thermodynamic process is entirely ruled out.

Complete molecular repose is a condition unknown to nature. But as soon as we restrict the movement of molecules to some extent, matter behaves in a remarkable manner. For example, the ability of molecules to form combinations with others falls off perceptibly when their speed is cut down. The action of sulfuric acid on sodium ceases at minus 80 degrees. At minus 110 degrees, sulfuric acid and hydrochloric acid no longer affect blue litmus paper. Even more remarkable—almost uncanny, in fact—is the behavior of certain metals and other substances when their temperatures are reduced still further. At 2 degrees above absolute zero, liquid helium suddenly shows a sharp increase in its capacity to conduct heat. Practically from one moment to the next, its heat-conductivity jumps a million times. In this condition, liquid helium is 300 times as good a conductor as silver, the best heat-conductor, and 800 times as good as copper. Substances in this state are called *superconductors*.

Another phenomenon observed at low temperatures is an enormous increase in electrical conductivity, the capacity to conduct electrons well. The electron is the smallest particle of electricity. The little atomic building stone carries a quite definite electrostatic charge. This, the smallest electric charge we know, is equivalent to 4.8025×10^{-10} electrostatic units or 1.602×10^{-19} coulombs. As we know, the hydrogen atom has only one electron in its shell. Because the nucleus of this atom carries an equally large positive electric charge, neither of the charges, positive or negative, will be outwardly in evidence. An atom of this kind is electrically neutral. If we take the single electron from a hydrogen atom, the atom is *ionized* and is found to be electrically charged. The external electric charge is measured at plus 4.8025×10^{-10} electrostatic units, which is sufficient to capture a "roaming" electron. An atom of iron has twenty-six electrons in its shell. A single phonograph needle contains trillions and trillions of them. If all the electrons in the phonograph needle could be removed, it would yield a charge capable of supplying a current of some hundreds of amperes for the duration of one second. In the normal course of events, however, only one to three electrons can be taken from an atom of iron. These are electrons racing about among atoms in an iron wire.

Metals such as copper, silver, and aluminum are good *conductors*. They readily convey current, or, rather, allow it to pass through them. The process does not, of course, require the carriers of the electricity—the electrons—to be pumped in at one end of the conductor and drawn off at the other. There is no need for electrons to be pumped into a wire because they are already there. They come from the shells of the atoms. If we now apply an electromotive force to the wire, it acts on the electrons like a suction pump.

The free electrons begin to travel. Their movement is not in the least erratic, but is directed at a definite goal: the positive electric pole of the electromotive force. This pole—consisting, like the wire, of metal—shows a shortage of electrons because the atoms at the pole piece are deficient in electrons. In an effort to remedy the situation, one section of the conductor wrests electrons from the neighboring section and incorporates them into its own structure.

However, because the source of current and the wire form a closed *circuit*, a system which in the electrical sense has neither a beginning nor an end, this plundering of electrons progresses from section to section. The result is a flow of current. The more easily the electrons can be detached from their atoms, the better the metal *conducts*. The case is different with substances whose atoms put up a strong resistance to any severing of the link between the nucleus and the electron shell. These are termed *bad conductors*. Their electrons have only slight freedom of movement. In the so-called *semiconductors* the movement of electrons is not entirely inhibited, but it does not allow any appreciable number of them to break away and roam.

Now it has been shown that even downright bad conductors of electricity, when refrigerated to a temperature of about minus 269 degrees centigrade, become extremely good conductors. This state is known as *superconductivity*. The resistance of electrolytic copper (very pure copper), for example, has been found to drop a million times when the metal is so treated. The electrical resistance of the superconductor falls so drastically that a wire a million miles long and only a thousandth of a millimeter in diameter would show a resistance of no more than three quarters of one ohm. It may be noted that a wire of that length would cover the distance between the earth and the moon four times. However, the enormous fall in resistance becomes evident from yet other phenomena. If an electric current is produced by magnetic induction in a superconductor shaped like a closed ring, the current will flow on undiminished for hours without being further excited. This is in no sense a matter of theory, having been proved by scientific experiment. It has been calculated that the electrical resistance in this case is 100,000 billion times less than under normal conditions. At a temperature of minus 271 degrees a lead-bismuth coil no more than one tenth of a millimeter in diameter could be loaded with a current of 500 amperes without getting warm. In the non-superconducting state the wire would be ripped to atoms and not a shred would be left.

We now know a substance called niobium nitride that becomes a superconductor not just short of absolute zero but 23 degrees earlier, at the temperature of liquid hydrogen. This substance, a compound of niobium metal and nitrogen, may revolutionize the entire field of electrical engineering. We have only to imagine a radio transmitter using an oscillation circuit made of a spiral or coils of supercooled niobium nitride. A current in this, once induced, would keep on flowing without further stimulation.

Solid into Liquid, Liquid into Gas

The limit of temperature to which an object can be heated while remaining a solid is determined by the binding energy of its constituent particles. By this we mean the cohesion of the atoms inside a molecule or in the crystal structure of a substance, either through the action of electrostatic forces or by means of one or more common pairs of electrons acting as a bond between two atoms. As we know, a piece of iron, for example, is built up of tiny little crystals; groups of eight atoms of iron "join hands" in this way to form small cubes. If we warm the iron, the atoms inside the miniature cubes begin to stir and stretch, and are forced out of their normal positions. Where there is a vast number of atoms—e.g., in an iron rod—the expansion of the intervals between the atoms can be measured. We recognize it from the expansion of the metal itself. If we keep up the supply of energy until the temperature of the iron is raised to about 500 degrees centigrade, the first visible red rays appear. The object begins to glow.

It might be asked why the iron first begins to glow at 500 degrees and not sooner. In actual fact, the iron does glow sooner, but we do not see the color of the glow for the sim-

ple reason that the rays being given off are infrared rays. At
1,500 degrees centigrade a remarkable thing happens. The
cohesion of the atoms within the tiny cubes has already become extremely weak. The atoms of iron tug and wrench at
the framework of the cubes, seemingly with the sole object
of breaking away from their "irksome" bonds. In the end,
the binding force fails altogether. Just as single crystals are
loosened from a lump of sugar by water, so the enormous
heat applied to the iron drives one atom after another out of
the cubes. The crystal lattice collapses like a house of cards,
and the iron melts. Of course, binding forces are still at
work in the molten mass. They still tie one atom to another,
but the link is loose and haphazard. The atoms of the molten
metal behave rather like peas that are being stirred vigor-
ously in a bowl with a spoon. If more power is now supplied, the process becomes tempestuous. The molten mass
begins to boil, and simultaneously the metal becomes white
hot. It may happen that individual atoms shoot off the surface.

Such an individual free atom behaves quite differently
from one that is tied to a second atom or to a group. For example, if energy is applied to this atom, it takes off like a
rocket and gains velocity as it flies through the air. However, this velocity cannot be boosted at will, because even in
the world of microphysics everything has its limits. The reason why an atom cannot be indefinitely accelerated lies in
its weight.

There is a strange relationship between the speed of a
particle and its mass. If we raise the velocity of an electron,
its mass increases. If we reduce the velocity, the mass decreases. If we were able to accelerate an electron until it
reached the speed of light, the mass would become infi-
nitely magnified. It would be possible to argue that if an
electron weighing 0.91×10^{-27} grams attained the speed
of light, it would become so heavy that it might bring the
earth crashing down out of its orbit. It would, in fact, be

heavier than the earth and everything in it. As the earth has remained in place to this day, we may take it as certain that no single electron has so far reached the speed of light.

What no electron has succeeded in doing is still more difficult for the lightest atomic nucleus—the hydrogen atom nucleus—which is 1,800 times heavier. The best we may reach is a speed closely approximating the speed of light. Once this maximum speed is attained, we shall achieve no appreciable increase in velocity, even if energy continues to be supplied. Part of the energy is then worked off in a different manner. It probably stimulates the atom to react in other ways—for example, by reducing its weight: the atom casts off part of its burden, a few electrons. Subsequently it may jettison some from its inner shells, and last of all, in extremity, electrons near the nucleus.

Why does the atom behave in this way? Quite simply because the energy that is no longer being used to achieve velocity cannot just be made to disappear without further ado. It is there, and because it is there, it produces effects. As a further increase in velocity is quite impossible, the energy attacks the electron shell and rips electrons out of it. In the process the atom becomes a little lighter and travels a little faster. However, the increase in velocity brought about in this way is of absolutely no account. Gradually, one by one, the electrons are thrown off. When an atom has lost all its electrons in this way and energy continues to be supplied, the atomic nucleus itself is in the end attacked. It is smashed into its constituent parts: neutrons and protons.

What Are the Temperatures at Man's Command?

Until about twenty years ago the range of temperatures at man's disposal was not particularly large. For a long time it went no higher than 2,700 degrees centigrade (4,900 degrees Fahrenheit). This is the region in which the smelting and welding of most metals and the vaporization of melts and liquids takes place. The temperature indicated is obtained by means of a mixture of one part of oxygen and two parts of hydrogen, which, when ignited, combine explosively to form water. Alternatively, it can be achieved with acetylene, a gas produced by the action of water on calcium carbide. Mixed with oxygen, this is used for welding iron and steel. The reaction heat developed in the burning of thermite, a mixture of powdered aluminum metal and ferric oxide, is several hundred degrees centigrade higher. The process involves the use of ignition agents developing high temperatures, such as potassium chlorate or barium peroxide. But what is the significance of 2,700 or even 3,000 degrees centigrade (4,900 or 5,500 degrees Fahrenheit) when there are substances that defy such temperatures?

Up to now it has never been possible with any flame temperature to melt the most heat-resistant of all substances: zirconium boride. It remains stubbornly solid even at 3,300 degrees centigrade (6,000 degrees Fahrenheit). But in this field, too, progress has been made. Recently a flame process using fluorine and hydrogen has been tested with which it proved possible at normal pressures to attain temperatures of 4,000 degrees centigrade (7,200 degrees Fahrenheit). When the gas pressure was raised to five atmospheres, the flame temperature was increased to 4,400 degrees centigrade (8,000 degrees Fahrenheit). By using this method with a further increase of pressure, we may soon produce flames with a centigrade temperature of 5,000 to 6,000 degrees centigrade (9,000 to 11,000 degrees Fahrenheit) at the core.

Considerably higher temperatures can be created by means of an electric arc, though only under special conditions. An arc of this kind is usually created when an electric current jumps the gap between two separated electrical conductors carrying different charges. The process that takes place is extremely interesting. Dry air, known as a good insulator, is not a conductor of electric current. It loses this property when it is ionized—i.e., when we expose the air to a high-tension electric field. All that is needed for this is a piece of wire connected to the positive pole of a source of electromotive force and a similar piece of wire at the negative pole, provided that they are kept face to face and some distance apart. The air between these two poles becomes ionized—that is, electrons are torn from the atoms in the molecules of air. Owing to their negative charge, these electrons strive to reach the end of the wire that is connected to the positive pole of the source of electromotive force. Meantime, the atoms in the molecules have acquired a positive charge through losing electrons; in other words, they have undergone positive ionization. They therefore strike out in the opposite direction, moving toward the end of the wire connected to the negative pole of the source of the electromotive force. On their way to the positive end the electrons use the molecules as springboards, leaping from atom to atom and from molecule to molecule. However, each time an electron lands on an atom and leaves it again, it causes the atom to give off radiation. If and when the density of electrons becomes so great that whole hosts of them hurl themselves at the atoms, the air becomes a conductor, and neutralization of the electric charges takes place with a flash that lights up the whole area. When this happens, the air develops such heat that temperatures of up to 4,000 degrees centigrade (7,200 degrees Fahrenheit) at the center of the arc are not infrequent. The use of a higher potential or stronger current has no effect other than to create a more brilliant arc. It does not cause a rise in temperature. If we wish to raise the temperature, we have to resort to certain expedients, such as focusing the arc.

This course was first adopted by K. Gerdien and G. Lotz in 1923. By passing the arc through a hole bored in a thick metal plate, they achieved a temperature of 10,000 degrees centigrade (18,000 degrees Fahrenheit) at the center of the arc. To prevent the metal from melting under the heat, they kept the plate continually sprayed with water. The current employed in these experiments was 600 amperes, thirty to sixty times the strength required for a normal arc. In 1951 Hans Bartels and K. Larenz of Hanover, using a current of "only" 500 amperes, attained a temperature of 34,000 degrees centigrade (61,000 degrees Fahrenheit). With 1,500 amperes H. Lochte-Hotgreven and Heinrich Maecker of the University of Kiel got as high as 50,000 degrees centigrade (90,000 degrees Fahrenheit) in 1952. Instead of using a hole bored in a metal plate, they passed their arc through a water pipe with an inside diameter of only three thirty-seconds of an inch. The carbon electrodes of the electric arc were made hollow to provide better facilities for observing the arc and for making exact temperature measurements.

A way of producing even higher temperatures has been found. The temperature of a gas, for instance, can be raised by forcing the molecules to move closer together. A cubic meter of moderately warm gas becomes very hot if we compress it rapidly into a volume corresponding to the contents of a thimble. Nevertheless, to heat such a gas to five million degrees centigrade (nine million degrees Fahrenheit), we should need to produce a pressure that is beyond the technical resources of man. Here, too, the physicists managed to find a way out. What could not be done with a gigantic pneumatic hammer, they thought, must be feasible with the aid of electric and magnetic fields. One way in which we can influence electrified atoms and molecules—so-called ions—is to expose them to such fields. By this means we can lead them around in a circle, accelerate them, or bring them to a standstill at will. Why, the scientists reasoned, should it not be possible to herd a number of ions of a gas into such a tight group as to bring about an enormous rise in temperature? It would simply be a matter of exposing them to a field produced by identical charges.

A group of British scientists working along these lines

succeeded in 1958 in heating a certain quantity of gas to five million degrees centigrade. If temperatures of this magnitude were to be maintained for fractions of a second, it was necessary to adopt entirely new methods of insulation for the containers in which the temperatures were to be produced.

The apparatus in which temperatures higher than the surface temperature of the sun were generated is called ZETA (Zero Energy Thermonuclear Assembly). It consists of a ring-shaped tube with an internal diameter of three feet and an over-all diameter of ten feet, and it is linked to the iron core of a large transformer. The tube contains heavy hydrogen that is accelerated by electromagnetic forces and compressed more and more by increase of current.

Heavy hydrogen, also called deuterium, differs from the "lighter" variety solely by reason of its greater weight. This, again, is due to the larger number of its constituent particles. Whereas the atomic nucleus of ordinary hydrogen consists of a single proton, the deuterium nucleus contains an additional neutron. As the neutron weighs approximately as much as the proton, the atomic nucleus of heavy hydrogen weighs roughly twice as much as that of ordinary hydrogen. In contrast to the electrically neutral neutron, which cannot be influenced by electrical or magnetic means, we have in deuterium a particle that not only possesses twice the mass of a neutron but can also be controlled by electric or magnetic fields. Such fields, applied in the ZETA apparatus, convert relatively cold hydrogen gas filling the entire tube into a fine hydrogen ring of dazzling whiteness that shows a temperature of five million degrees centigrade at its center. Be that as it may, the aim of these experiments—to use temperatures of this order to fuse atomic nuclei—was not achieved.

By exposing nuclei of heavy hydrogen to temperatures of five million degrees centigrade, it had been thought possible to force them into intimate union. Two of these nuclei, it was reasoned, would in the end produce one atomic nucleus of helium, and a pretty considerable amount of energy would be left over. It was this energy which was the object of so much attention. As already said, the aim was not achieved. The "fragment of a star" which the researchers thought they had in their hands remained what it was—a garishly glowing gas, but nonetheless a gas that had been heated to five million degrees centigrade.

"Fear No More the Heat o' the Sun"

No one knew how the vast energy of the sun was generated until in 1938–9 Hans A. Bethe of Cornell University put forward a satisfactory theory. Bethe asserted that the energy of the sun is the product of a cycle. On the sun, hydrogen produces helium, and energies are released in the process which are sufficient to make good the sun's loss of heat for billions of years to come. By means of these processes the sun is able to give off daily quantities of heat corresponding to an output of 500,000 quintillion horsepower. The temperatures developed inside the sun are of the order of 20 million degrees centigrade (36 million degrees Fahrenheit). The nucleus of a helium atom consists of a total of four nuclear particles of roughly equal weight: two protons and two neutrons. Protons and neutrons are differentiated above all by the electric charge that the proton carries while the neutron does not. To put it more exactly, in the case of the neutron the electric charge is *neutralized*—i.e., electrically screened in such a way that it has no outward action. Circumstances often nullify the neutralization, and the neutron then turns into a proton, losing one electron in the process. Similarly, a neutron can become a proton by capturing an electron. Protons are present in considerable quantities in the hydrogen sphere of the fixed stars and of the sun; in fact, more than two thirds of the sun's volume

consists of hydrogen nuclei. Nevertheless, without a contact substance—a catalyst, as it is called in chemistry—the
formation of nuclei of helium atoms cannot proceed. In
chemical processes such contact substances do not form
permanent compounds with other substances, but they accelerate the reactions. In the production of helium on the
sun, the role of catalyst is performed by carbon.

Bethe pictured the process in this way. An ordinary carbon nucleus with an atomic weight of 12 absorbs a hydrogen nucleus (proton), and by so doing becomes a nitrogen
nucleus with an atomic weight of 13. This nitrogen atom is
not stable: by dropping a positron, a positive electron, the
atom decays to form a carbon isotope with an atomic
weight of 13. This isotope again absorbs a hydrogen nucleus and so is transformed into a nitrogen nucleus with an
atomic weight of 14. By taking in a further hydrogen nucleus, the nitrogen is transformed into oxygen (15), an isotope that decays after a while to become nitrogen (15). The
nitrogen isotope now captures the last proton, splits into a
carbon nucleus (12) and a helium nucleus (4), and the carbon can immediately resume its role of catalyst.

As the cycle occurs on the sun, it takes billions of years
for the nucleus of a carbon atom and four hydrogen nuclei
to form a helium nucleus. But as a vast number of such cycles begin and end inside the sun every moment, the radiant
energy produced pours off its surface incessantly at the rate
of twenty horsepower per square inch. As a model for reproduction by man on earth, this process was ruled out
from the beginning. As the sun's cycle takes too long, it was
necessary to look about for another cycle.

It was found that helium nuclei can also be built up when
heavy and superheavy hydrogen in the presence of a sufficiently large quantity of normal hydrogen are exposed to
the kind of temperature generated in the explosion of an
ordinary atomic bomb. As we already know, the nucleus of
a heavy hydrogen atom consists of a proton and a neutron.

Superheavy hydrogen is made up of a proton with two neutrons. The effect of this arrangement is that this nucleus is three times as heavy as the normal hydrogen nucleus. Because it contains three atomic building blocks, it has been given the name *tritium*. If any means can be found of fusing normal hydrogen with a tritium nucleus, the result is a nucleus consisting of two neutrons and two protons. Such a nucleus is identical with that of the helium atom. But nuclear particles of atoms cannot be fused as easily as all that. Fusion on this scale calls for temperatures that, as already indicated, occur for brief periods in the course of atom-bomb explosions. The first man who ventured to make the attempt was the Hungarian-born American scientist Edward Teller. His formula: place certain quantities of light, medium-heavy, and heavy hydrogen in a thick-walled container and detonate an atomic bomb in it. The products are a quantity of helium, which is of no account, and a vast amount of radiant energy accompanied by temperatures never before generated—in short, the hydrogen bomb, which, upon detonation, develops a temperature of 20 million degrees centigrade (36 million degrees Fahrenheit).

The process that takes billions of years on the sun is here compressed into a fraction of a second. In the course of it the formation of no more than a gram of helium from hydrogen nuclei releases 200,000 kilowatt hours of energy, enough to supply the needs of the lighting system of a major city for several weeks. This illustration may perhaps bring home to us what happens when hydrogen is converted into helium not by the gram but by the ton.

Man now faces the task of directing his mastery of nuclear fusion to peaceful ends. The snag is this: how can an action that takes place in a flash be so slowed down that it can be brought under technical control? A means must be found of stretching the time it takes to convert hydrogen into helium in such a way that the energy is released not instantaneously, as in the case of the hydrogen bomb, but by degrees. If that is achieved, man will be rid of his power worries for all time. Hydrogen, the raw material of this new energy, is virtually inexhaustible, and the hydrogen isotope required to go with it—deuterium—is considerably easier to procure than uranium 235 or plutonium. When the day of achievement comes, there will never be a power shortage again. Power will be so cheap that it will be possible to tackle practically any project that has so far been deferred because power was lacking. Moreover, the danger of radioactive injury from power production by this method is materially less than it is in the conventional atomic-power plants of today.

Electricity from Sunlight

The actual amount of heat given off by the sun has long been the subject of careful study. It has been established at approximately 100 septillion calories per second (one septillion $= 1 \times 10^{24}$). In terms of electrical energy, that is equivalent to some 0.5 septillion kilowatt hours. This amount of energy would melt a block of one million cubic meters of ice in a single second. If we fix the price per kilowatt hour at no more than two cents, the energy radiated by the sun every second would cost about 1×10^{22}. That sum represents more money and goods than the earth has ever had. Of this vast output of energy the earth receives "only" one two-billionth part. The radiation reaching all the other planets taken together does not total more than 0.001 per cent. Consequently, 99.99 per cent of the sun's rays are swallowed up in space. To gain an idea of the proportion that reaches the earth, let us picture an area the size of West Virginia which is suddenly the scene of a cloudburst. The rain that falls on the roof of a small home represents approximately one two-billionth part of the total precipitation.

Every square yard of the earth's surface on which the sun shines receives about one kilowatt of power. Accordingly, if we assume a figure of 1,000 hours of sunshine per annum, a small house with a roof area of only 500 square feet would receive no less than 50,000 kilowatt hours of power. That is roughly equivalent to the heat generated by five tons of coal, or approximately the amount of coal required to keep the steam heating of a house in operation through a winter. The amount of solar energy which falls on a sunlit surface of only eight square miles would be sufficient to supply the total power needs of Germany. The time may not be far distant when large parts of the earth, particularly in the tropics, will draw their power supplies from solar-electric sources or solar-thermal power plants.

Efforts are constantly being made to harness the sun's energy. The Russians, for example, tried for some time with giant rolled-glass mirrors embedded in concrete frames. According to their reports, they succeeded by this means in heating steam to a temperature of 468 degrees centigrade (874 degrees Fahrenheit). Another arrangement—solar reflectors made of glass and plywood which were developed for use in Central Asia—produced a steam pressure of 165 pounds per square inch at a temperature of 186 degrees centigrade (366 degrees Fahrenheit). The appliances developed for Central Asia are said to have worked very well. Noteworthy experiments by French scientists have also touched off a good deal of discussion. Like the Russians, the French work on the principle of using the sun's rays to vaporize liquids. Other experiments have attempted to smelt metals by direct solar heat. The procedure adopted is to catch sunlight in a large plane mirror about forty feet wide and to direct it onto a large parabolic mirror. The virtually parallel rays that fall on the first mirror are concentrated at a single point by the parabolic mirror. At this point, known as the focal point, inflammable materials easily catch fire. This effect, the concentration of maximum heat at the focal point, is used to boil water or smelt metals. If, for example, a ball-shaped tank is set up at the focal point of the mirror and water is allowed to circulate slowly in it, the water becomes very hot. In various arrangements of this kind, temperatures at the focal point of up to 2,500 degrees centigrade (4,500 degrees Fahrenheit) have been measured. Applying temperature generated by the sun's heat alone, the French have succeeded in smelting about 130 pounds of iron an hour.

France already possesses solar power plants. One of these is located near the village of Mont Louis in the Pyrenees, another in Algeria. At both plants, large aluminum mirrors are used to intercept and focus the sun's rays. Thousands of much smaller models for domestic purposes, so to speak, are in use in India in the form of *solar cooking stoves*. They serve the Indian housewife as a cheap replacement for a fuel-burning stove. On her solar stove the Indian woman cooks rice, boils water for tea, and fries eggs, all without ever having to tend a fire.

In America the leading expert on solar power plants is Charles G. Abbot of the Smithsonian Institution. He too uses parabolic mirrors, with liquids heated at the focal point. Their heat is then conveyed to water, and this is converted into steam. Steam drives a turbine, and the turbine supplies electric current. Another project for the utilization of solar energy would abandon parabolic mirrors altogether, as their manufacturing costs increase with their size, and would replace them with a large number of smaller reflectors, such as ordinary small plane mirrors. Many thousands of these mirrors can be set up in open country, or better still in a valley, and so disposed that the sun's rays are reflected onto a globe-shaped water tank raised on metal supports somewhere near the center of the layout. If the reflectors are skillfully arranged, an approximately uniform amount of solar energy can be concentrated on the tank, whatever the position of the sun. In desert regions alone such methods could produce up to half a million kilowatt hours of electrical energy per acre annually.

Means also exist for converting sunlight directly into electrical energy. The first attempts to do this date back to 1880. In that year the first *selenium cells* were constructed; these early models consisted to all intents and purposes of fine platinum-plated silver wires with a selenium coating. The American Charles Sumner Tainter used metallic selenium, which he obtained from the vitreous, non-metallic form by heating it to 100 degrees centigrade (212 degrees Fahrenheit). This form proved to be a semiconductor of electricity with the strange property of having a certain degree of light-sensitivity related to its electrical conductivity. It became clear that the electrical conductivity greatly increased when the metal was exposed to light, rapidly dropping again when the light was removed. If such a cell were connected to a galvanometer and exposed to light, the electricity produced by the light could be directly measured. The current generated by light in cells of this kind was naturally extremely small. At best, it amounted to a millionth of an ampere and a thousandth of a volt. Very precise instruments were therefore needed to measure the current and the voltage. A billion of these cells would have had to be linked together to produce one watt.

The *photoelectric cell*, as it is called, has been substantially improved in Germany; but the energy output of even the most sophisticated of these cells is still far too small to drive a low-powered motor. Even today a photoelectric cell about two inches in diameter, on exposure to sunlight, delivers no more than a few milliamperes of current at one tenth of a volt. In other words, the output is still so low that it would not be sufficient to light a small flashlight bulb. Yet, for all their small yield, these photoelectric cells have acquired great importance in industry and technology. They are employed as exposure meters, as calorimeters, as reflectometers, and glossmeters. They are also incorporated in control systems. They serve as controls for machines, for opening and closing doors, and for switching on and off street lighting and store-window lighting. They also form part of the security arrangements for strongrooms and safes.

In the search for more effective ways of converting sunlight into electric power, American scientists have struck out in another direction. This has led to the creation of phototransistors. The structure of these transistors is in itself staggeringly simple, but their manufacture is still bound up with great difficulties. The apparatus in question consists of a semiconductor against which two fine metal points are pressed.

What does one of these semiconductors look like, seen from the electrical point of view? We should picture it as a collection of atoms, some of which have retained their full complement of electrons in their atom shells, while others show "holes." The electrons that should be found in the holes in the atoms are now free. They move around inside the semiconductor, but their movement is by no means erratic. They seek out atoms close at hand that likewise have holes in their shells. One of these electrons will jump into the vacant hole, and so fill a gap. When they make the jump, they leave behind another hole. This in turn is filled by another electron that has similarly left a hole somewhere. In this way, a sort of game develops which can be compared to the children's game called puss-in-the-corner. If we consider the proceeding as a whole, it is actually not the electrons that travel, but the holes. They move in the opposite direction right through the formation of atoms. However, since, according to the laws of electronics, a hole in an atom shell caused by the absence of an electron is tantamount to the presence of a positive electric charge, in practical terms the "stream of holes" will be propagated in exactly the same way as a stream of electrons. The only difference is that the direction of propagation is not toward the positive pole but the opposite way—toward the negative pole of the source of current. In other words, the behavior of the stream of holes is the precise opposite of that of the stream of electrons.

As we have seen, the electrical conductivity—or, to put it the other way around, the electrical resistance—of a body is to a large extent dependent on external conditions such as temperature, the voltage applied, or incoming light. If, now, a substance is chosen which is sensitive to light, the light can be transformed into electrical energy. Light quanta continually hammer electrons out of atom shells, so giving rise to the holes already mentioned. The more electrons punched out and the more holes created, the greater is the stream of holes, and therefore the greater the electrical energy obtained.

In the phototransistors that have been developed in the United States for such purposes, the basic element used is silicon. Silicon occurs in vast quantities in nature—always in combination with oxygen—in the form of silicon dioxide and in silicates. About twenty-five per cent of the outer crust of the earth consists of this element. We find silicon in almost all types of rock. Free silicon is isolated by fusing quartz sand with coke in an electric oven. The material obtained in this way is naturally not suitable for phototransistors. It has been found that only the completely pure element is of practical use.

In the very first experiments with this, the energy from the "stream of holes" in the silicon crystal proved to be strong enough to light a small flashlight bulb. Later experiments produced sufficient current to power small motors or small radio transmitters. The energy generated was enough to ensure reception of signals from the transmitter over a distance of eight miles. Within a short period it became possible to raise the efficiency of such solar batteries from one to six per cent. Now the figure is eleven per cent, and it is expected that we may soon be able to boost it to as much as twenty or twenty-five per cent. This means that a solar battery with a total area of a square yard will provide an output of approximately 200 to 250 watts. If the sunlit roof of a house some 650 square feet in area were covered with phototransistors, they would yield fifteen kilowatts of power. A large number of these transistors, arranged side by side, make up a battery, and with appropriate wiring, voltages and currents of almost any size can be obtained. The deciding factor is the number of transistors. The energy supplied by them could be stored during the day in accumulators and used at night for lighting purposes. It has been calculated that if a normal household had a solar battery about 100 square feet in area, enough current would be produced to supply the needs of the whole family.

Solar batteries of the kind used at present in the United States to supply current to rural telephone networks are still relatively expensive because they require very pure silicon. The pure material, processed into wafers about as thin as a razor blade, still costs almost as much as the equivalent amount of gold.

In future this development will be carried a step further. Pure silicon will be deposited on mica or some other insulating material by vaporization because there is no need for the film to be any thicker than some hundredths of a millimeter. Such a method may one day reduce the price of these batteries considerably. The time may come when conventional roof tiles will be replaced by tiles of glass with a fine coating of silicon. We are certain to find other materials that will increase the efficiency of solar batteries. Already small toy cars are being driven by sunlight. From four to six phototransistors about the size of a silver dollar supply sufficient current to drive the small electric motor. We may live to see the day when our own cars are powered by solar energy.

The latest developments show that direct sunlight is not necessary for the operation of a solar battery. It will produce current even by ordinary daylight, though the output is, of course, correspondingly smaller. It would already be feasible to supply any house with electric current obtained from sunlight. This would reduce the load on the municipal light and power networks, which would then need to supply power only for industrial plants and workshops. Unhappily, such plans remain to be realized. Yet the project would demand only a fraction of the expenditure that has already been poured out on atomic-energy research. The development of solar energy could revolutionize the whole future of electric power. Territories such as the Sahara could be transformed into fertile land by the installation of giant solar batteries. In practice, this could be achieved with materials that are present on the spot in inexhaustible quantity, for the raw material of silicon is sand, the very sand that turned the Sahara into a desert.

Infrared Photography

Experiments in photography with infrared sensitive plates were first made about thirty years ago. At that time emulsions were found which could be used to sensitize photographic plates and films to infrared rays. In the course of these experiments the photographer encountered all sorts of surprises. For instance, he succeeded in taking photographs over a distance of sixty miles. That in itself was nothing unusual; but on the days on which these photographs were taken the air was so misty that visibility was reduced to a maximum of twenty miles. In spite of this, mountains sixty miles away from the position of the camera could be seen clearly and distinctly in the photographs. They looked as if there had been no mist barrier of any sort to impede visibility. Naturally, these experiments were pursued and led to further surprises. Flat country, meadows, and woodland where leaf plants grew showed up in a different way from the normal. They looked very bright, almost white. Heavily rusted ironwork likewise produced a lighter effect, but so did the complexions of dark-skinned people. By contrast, the blue of the sky and of water surfaces turned out very dark.

Experimenters asked themselves what the cause of these unfamiliar contrasts could be. Was it that chlorophyll reflected the invisible heat rays so intensely that they darkened the photographic plate more strongly? This could not be so: there must be another reason for the peculiar reproduction of the leaf green because chlorophyll transmits infrared rays. It turned out to be the air contained in the leaf plants which causes total reflection of the infrared rays, in the course of which the rays re-emerge on the top side of the leaf. Water, on the other hand, absorbs infrared radiation, making the water surfaces of the earth appear dark. Air shows varying properties of absorption. Moist air soaks up more heat than dry air because mist and moisture are receptive to heat. But even moisture brought out remarkable differences. It was shown that mist droplets of a specific size absorbed considerably more infrared rays than others with a smaller or larger diameter. Soon a relationship was found between the diameter of the mist droplets and the wave length of the infrared rays they absorbed. In cases where the wave length corresponded to the diameter of the mist droplets, the infrared rays were almost entirely absorbed. The droplets thereupon developed so-called resonance vibrations, consuming the entire energy of the rays.

Realization of these facts led to the discovery of *gaps* in the atmosphere which behaved like windows, as it were, allowing only certain wave lengths in the infrared range to pass through. Once the existence of these gaps was known, it was not difficult to develop special photographic material by which perfect photography through mist and fog was made possible. However, in photography with infrared-sensitive film stock, another point of great importance is

SOUTHWEST MIAMI HIGH SCHOOL

that the objects to be photographed should themselves give off heat or be exposed to heat. In nature, light sources of the kind necessary for infrared photographs are found practically everywhere. Daylight and our own artificial sources of light contain sufficient long-wave light rays for the purpose. For pure infrared photographs, visible light is not needed at all. In fact, efforts are made to exclude it by means of appropriate filters. All that is required to "light" a dark room with infrared rays is a fire in the fireplace, a hot iron, sometimes even a heating pad or a hot radiator.

The moon plays a great part in outdoor infrared photography, particularly at night. It need not necessarily be visible to us; it may even be overcast by a thick cloud layer. The reason is that moonlight has been found to contain up to seventy-five per cent of dark infrared light. This proportion has been compared with the infrared radiation from a hot 500-watt iron operating at a distance of about twenty-five yards. The moon acts like an infrared searchlight of huge dimensions. This was observed during World War II when the quality of night photographs taken in reconnaissance aircraft was found to be dependent, in the last analysis, on infrared radiation emanating from the moon.

Just as the archaeologist finds valuable evidence of ancient times in ruins, the paleontologist—the student of fossils—regards the fossilized remains of plants and animals as biological witnesses of a vanished epoch of the earth. They provide him with information about the ages of the earth's strata, about their former composition, about the climate prevailing at various periods, and supply pointers to the flora and fauna of those early times. But, to the sorrow of the paleontologists, fossils and impressions of plants and animals often fail to stand out from their background with sufficient clarity. Frequently their shape is only vaguely outlined.

Infrared photography works wonders in lifting out faint,

indistinct, and blurred shapes from the surrounding surfaces. This is possible because the fossilized contours and the
background reflect infrared light in varying degrees. Photographs made in this magic light by experts reveal many details that in normal light would remain invisible. Similarly,
infrared photography used in connection with archaeologi-
cal finds has established many facts that would have escaped
the eye in ordinary light.

The crime laboratories of any modern police force are
equipped with infrared and ultraviolet lamps,[2] one of whose
uses is the detection of forgeries.

Take the case of a document stamped by the forger with
an "official" seal over the place where there had originally
been writing. The color of the stamp ink was the same as
that used by officials. What the forger did not know, however, was that this particular stamp ink contained no oil. As
oil-free ink does not reflect infrared light, the invisible rays
"wiped away" the superimposed seal and laid bare the writing beneath. The same method can be used to expose a
forger who attempts, say, to pass off a forged letter, check,
or handwritten will, as genuine. Iron-gallate inks and log-
wood inks, such as are still occasionally used, and copying-
ink script remain clearly visible under infrared light, while
characters written with pure aniline-dye inks vanish.

Bona-fide dealers and other persons frequently buy cars
or trucks that turn out to have been stolen. Usually the
numbers of the chassis and the engine have been filed away
or hammered out. Finding the original number is therefore
often difficult. In such cases the first attempt to identify the
number is made by chemical methods. If these fail, X rays
or ultraviolet rays or infrared rays will usually succeed.

Nevertheless, certain rare cases of forgery cannot be
solved by even the most subtle methods. One occurred during World War II when the Nazi government forged Brit-

[2] See p. 68.

ish banknotes to the value of nearly £200,000,000. Made by expert craftsmen who were held in a concentration camp, these facsimiles were for a long time not recognized as fakes in neutral countries. Even the watermark and the paper were exact replicas of those used by the Bank of England. At the end of the war the Bank of England had to issue new banknotes (those with the famous silver line) to prevent the nation's currency from being wrecked by the circulation of counterfeit notes that stood up to every kind of test. The German counterfeiters, using every available aid, had even resorted to ultraviolet light and infrared rays; in other words, the forgers had—for a while, at least—defeated their victims with the victims' own weapons.

Some years ago the French customs authorities confiscated a small package consigned to an address in Portugal which contained some very valuable stamps. The consignor, a Signor Sperati, son of an Italian colonel and grandson of a general, was charged with evasion of the customs and sentenced to pay a fine of 300,000 francs. He protested that the stamps so heavily assessed for duty purposes were fakes, and consequently worth much less. The fine was therefore reduced to 20,000 francs.

At this point the public prosecutor intervened; it happened that at about the same time a Swedish collector had brought an action against Sperati for having sold him a faked rare 1855 stamp. The public prosecutor called experts as witnesses, who then examined the stamp by the most modern methods, including ultraviolet and infrared rays. On their evidence, the rare Swedish stamp was genuine. Nevertheless—and this is a curiosum in the annals of crime—Sperati demonstrated that it was a forgery. He argued that he was an artist whose object was to lend a helping hand to people with incomplete collections by supplying them with "good imitations" at moderate prices. The court acquitted him.

Philatelists all over the world raised a storm. If there

existed a man who could forge stamps so skillfully that experts could not distinguish the genuine from the false, then surely most collections were valueless. Rumor has it that a group of British philatelists finally "bought" Sperati, acquiring his collection (with all the fakes thrown in) for a substantial sum of money, on condition that he would not manufacture any more fake stamps or initiate anyone into the secrets of his methods. Quite obviously he had used infrared rays—by means of which, in normal circumstances, fakes can be instantly distinguished from genuine issues—in the production of the forgeries.

Some years ago an action was brought against the police of a big European city for causing bodily harm. The plaintiff claimed that a policeman had beaten him so hard with a rubber truncheon that he had suffered severe effusions of blood on his back and upper arm. An effusion of blood is caused when blood vessels are torn by a blow or by pressure and the blood seeps into the surrounding tissue. It is recognizable by a reddening of the skin over the area. In time these discolored patches usually turn blue, green, and yellow, and seem after a while to disappear altogether.

The police officer declared under oath that he had not struck the plaintiff at all. More than a year had gone by since the incident, and a medical examination would be unlikely to reveal evidence of an effusion of blood. The examining physician failed, in fact, to discover any suspicious marks. The case would have been dismissed, had the plaintiff not previously testified under oath. The public prosecutor decided to call in a physicist specializing in criminology to establish the facts. The physicist was aware, of course, that infrared radiation penetrates the skin more efficiently than visible light, and is in part reflected back by the tissue underneath. But would the blood likewise throw back the long-wave rays? An infrared photograph of the plaintiff's back and arm was taken, and there, standing out quite clearly in it, were weals and bruises of the kind caused by hard blows. This amazing result led to an immediate verdict against the policeman.

The network of veins under the skin can be recorded in clear, high-contrast photographs by the infrared method. In the case of some people with very thin skins, the main branches of this network of veins are, of course, visible to the naked eye; but in all cases only an infrared photograph can bring out the details.

Measuring Atoms and Molecules with an Infrared Spectrometer

As we know, atoms in an excited state give off electromagnetic radiation in the form of light and heat. But we also know that the energy absorbed must be available in a definite quantum. Only then is it accepted by the atom. When one of the electrons jumps from the excited level to a lower level, roughly the same amount of this absorbed energy is set free again. As atoms—and, of course, molecules as well—are constantly being "excited," they continually give off rays, usually heat rays. Infrared radiation is often very weak, and measuring it accurately calls for special instruments.

An instrument with which heat rays can be measured with the utmost precision is the *bolometer*, so named because in Greek *bolē* is equivalent to "ray." Bolometers have been known for a comparatively long time.

The first instrument of the kind, a "resistance bridge" invented by the American Samuel Pierpont Langley (1834–1906), consisted of four fine, blackened iron wires. They formed the branches of a very sensitive measuring instrument that operates on the zero principle. When no current is flowing through the instrument, the needle of a galvanometer connected to it shows no deflection. In Langley's bridge, two of the wires were connected to a small battery, and the other two to the terminals of a sensitive galvanometer. When a beam of light was directed at one of the wires through a narrow slit, the wire was heated. This altered the electrical resistance, and the electrical equilibrium on the bridge was thereby upset, so that a current was set up in one arm of the bridge and deflected the needle of the galvanometer. In course of time this instrument was naturally improved, and nowadays platinum strips are used in place of iron wires. Usually they are less than half an inch long, about one thirtieth of an inch wide, and no more than four millionths of an inch thick.

The most sensitive bolometers are obtained when certain metals are cooled until they become superconductors. As we have already seen, for all practical purposes the current flowing in metal under these conditions never decreases. If, then, the bridge device is so arranged that no current flows through the galvanometer, the effect of the smallest amount of heat on the metal will be to remove the state of superconductivity at once, and the electrical resistance in one arm of the bridge will jump sharply. By this method the most minute quantities of heat can be measured.

The function of the bolometer is also applied in the study of molecules. If energy is used to excite the molecules, part of the energy is absorbed. If the composition of the heat radiation emanating from the molecule in question is now tested with a sensitive bolometer, certain wave lengths are found to be absent. This is due to the fact that every type of atom absorbs infrared radiation of a definite frequency. But as molecules are built up of several different types of atom, a specific infrared spectrum results. Accordingly, the grouping of atoms in the molecule can be established on the basis of the wave lengths absorbed.

In the course of research on these lines it has been found that the structure of molecules follows five patterns. The atoms in the molecule of carbonic acid, for instance, are laid out in a straight line. The atoms in a water molecule form a triangle with an angle of 105 degrees; those of ammonia a pyramid, with the three hydrogen atoms at the base and the nitrogen atom at the apex. A methane molecule takes the form of a tetrahedron in which the carbon atom is situated at the center of gravity and the hydrogen atoms at the four corners. And a benzene molecule is represented as a closed ring of six carbon atoms, each of which is associated with one hydrogen atom.

The bolometer has long been used by astronomers to determine temperatures on distant stars. For example, bolometer studies have been made of heat radiation reaching the earth from Arcturus, a star in the constellation of Boötes. The studies involve measurement of heat no greater than eleven billionths of the heat given off by an ordinary candle a yard away. In the cases of other stars, readings of heat radiation have been made which were five billion times smaller.

CHAPTER 3

Ultraviolet Rays:
The Dark Light

In 1893 Niels Ryberg Finsen, a thirty-three-year-old physician in Copenhagen, stood at the window of his home watching a cat as it lay on the roof of a lower house across the street. Everybody knows that cats love sun and warmth, so that at first there was nothing remarkable about the animal on the roof. But the doctor saw that the cat was lying on the boundary line between the light and the shadow thrown by a wall, and he observed that whenever the shadow reached its body, it turned toward the light. This fact in itself would likewise have had no special significance. But the cat was obviously ill—its every movement was languid and feeble. Why had it lain down in the sun? This, the doctor thought, must have something to do with the light, because the cat could just as well have found warmth by the stove. Finsen's interest was aroused, and he began to stage various experiments.

First he exposed frogs' eggs to ordinary sunlight, and then to filtered sunlight. He filtered the light by passing it through different pieces of transparent colored glass. When red light was directed at them, the frog embryos in the eggshells only gradually turned toward it. Under blue-violet light their reactions were very lively. Finsen counted up to ninety-six changes of position in half an hour. Blue-violet light was therefore biologically more effective than red light. Both chemically and biologically, however, the effects of the dark portion of the solar spectrum adjoining the violet light proved even stronger.

This dark portion was discovered in 1801 by the German physicist Johann Wilhelm Ritter and was named *ultra-violet* radiation. This radiation is, among other things, the real cause of the severe burns suffered by mountain climbers and skiers and sometimes, too, by sunbathers when they stay in the sun too long. Snow blindness, a widespread condition among inhabitants of the polar regions, is also due to ultraviolet rays, but its effects are harmful only to persons who have been exposed to the rays too long. Taken in small doses, they are healthy and beneficial.

For a long period countless small children were the victims of a frightful scourge known as rickets. This is a condition in which the growing bone becomes soft and stunted owing to calcium deficiency. Children afflicted with it have difficulty in learning to walk, and in particularly serious cases the chest, pelvis, and legs become deformed. Strangely enough, children affected by this disease were not confined to countries with climatic disadvantages, such as Britain, Norway, Sweden, and Finland; it occurred equally in France, Spain, Italy, and even North Africa. Indeed, the fact that rickets was an ancient disease was made plain by a number of Egyptian mummies that displayed marked deformities of rachitic origin. Long before vitamins were known, it was suspected that a connection existed between diet and rachitic disorders.

But was poor diet really the sole cause of this illness? Had not a well-known zoologist pointed out at the beginning of the century that lack of sunlight might give rise to rickets? How had he come upon an idea so far removed from the thought of his time? He had observed that animals at the zoo which were kept in sunless quarters contracted rickets, while others living in sunny enclosures remained immune.

In 1919 an epidemic of rickets broke out in Germany, claiming thousands of victims, particularly among small children. This was not to be wondered at in a Germany short of milk, butter, and other nourishment. Thanks to the magnificent work of the Quakers, the epidemic was brought to a standstill by large donations of food. But even after years had passed, more than a third of all the children involved still bore visible traces of the disease.

At the time of the outbreak in 1919 a Berlin doctor recalled the observations of the zoologist in question. He established that it was possible to combat rickets in children by giving them regular treatment with sunlight or, better still, with ultraviolet light. Conclusive evidence came from the results of experiments made by Harry Steenbock, an American biochemist.

Dr. Steenbock owned a goat that not only supplied him with milk but also served him, figuratively speaking, as a guinea pig for study purposes. He was particularly interested in the processes of metabolism in the living body. He kept the animal under constant observation and practically confined to its shed. His object was to ensure that the goat ate nothing that had not previously been accurately weighed and examined. One day he discovered that the animal was excreting more calcium than it took in with its food. As the feed was carefully put together, he asked himself where the excess calcium in the excreta could come from. The solution to the riddle was to be found in Germany.

The chemist Adolf Windaus of Göttingen had discovered a substance formed by certain plants which he called *ergosterol*. This substance is first broken down chemically in the bodies of animals and human beings. By way of two further intermediate products in a complicated process, it produces another substance of great biological effectiveness, the vitamin D. However, the conversion of ergosterol into vitamin D in human or animal bodies comes about only when the skin is exposed to sunlight or, more precisely, to the influence of the ultraviolet light contained in sunlight. That was how the clue to the cause of calcium deficiency and rickets was found.

Vitamin D, formed under the influence of ultraviolet light, discharges an extremely important function in our bodies. It is responsible for the firmness of our bone matter. It is the agent by which mineral salts that enter the body by way of foodstuffs are brought into proper proportion with one another. The result is the formation of a cement that knits the bone matter together. When there is a lack of adequate ultraviolet radiation—in winter, for example— the ergosterol in our skin cannot be converted into vitamin D. This brings bone formation to a halt, whereupon the calcium already deposited in the bones is absorbed into the blood stream and is excreted as a product of metabolism. This information provided the solution to the mystery of Dr. Steenbock's goat: the excess calcium in its excreta was derived from its own bones.

Rickets has lost its terror for us. A case of incipient rickets can often be cured simply by sunbaths or by ultraviolet-ray treatment. When, as in the dark winter months, sunlight is not abundant, we resort to artificial ultraviolet lamps.

The Protective Ultraviolet Filter

We are apt to forget that we live at the bottom of an ocean of air, and that the atmosphere lies between us and the lethal reaches of outer space. The air in the atmosphere which supplies us with indispensable oxygen performs another important function: it protects us against dangerous rays that originate on the surface of the sun. Certain strata of air in the stratosphere at distances of twenty to forty-five miles from the earth reduce the intensity of a large proportion of the rays to a point where they no longer constitute an immediate danger to us.

It is well known that the strength of ultraviolet rays increases with altitude. The higher we climb, the more dangerous to us they become. This increase in the strength of radiation at great heights is attributed to the fact that the distance traveled by the rays through the air is shorter and that the thinner air therefore weakens them less. Thus, the proportion of ultraviolet light in sunlight at a height of 5,000 feet above sea level is twenty-five per cent greater than at 1,700 feet. The decisive factor, however, is the wave length of these invisible light rays. To get an approximate yardstick for the extent of the entire ultraviolet range, we may compare the range of the visible light spectrum with an area the size of the state of Oregon, and that of ultraviolet rays with the combined area of Minnesota and Iowa.

For practical purposes, the ultraviolet rays have been divided up into three large groups. We distinguish between the A group, with wave lengths of 0.000315 to 0.0004 millimeters, and the B group, with wave lengths of 0.000280 to 0.000315 millimeters, while the group of rays with wave lengths of less than 0.000280 millimeters is labeled C. Sometimes this latter range is further subdivided into ultraviolet C_1 (0.000280 to 0.000240 millimeters) and ultraviolet C_2 (0.000240 to 0.000220 millimeters). However, the radiation from the sun embraces yet another range of short-wave ultraviolet light. Its wave length fluctuates between .000220 and 0.0000136 millimeters.

The very short-wave ultraviolet rays of the sun never get closer to the earth than a distance of thirty-five miles. At that height a curious process takes place. Between about twenty-five and forty-five miles above the earth, and some-

times at even greater heights, there are strata of pure oxygen. These strata are constantly shifting, first to a higher
level, then to a lower. On the dark side of the earth, the
side where it is night, we find this oxygen in molecular
form. These molecules consist of three atoms of oxygen
held together by electrical binding forces.

The moment the first ray of sunlight penetrates the
stratum, a process begins which saves us from serious burns.
The sunlight brings with it extremely short-wave ultraviolet rays. At full intensity these would be strong enough
to burn up all life on earth in a matter of seconds. But long
before they reach the surface of the earth, high up at a level
of thirty miles, they enter the ionosphere. There they encounter oxygen molecules, which they break up. Under the
influence of the constant flow of ultraviolet rays now pouring down, three each of these ionized oxygen atoms combine to form an extremely active molecule. The ozone
molecule so formed is capable of breaking down again very
rapidly into an ordinary oxygen molecule and an oxygen
atom. In this way the entire oxygen belt around the earth to
a height of between thirty and forty-five miles is transformed under the influence of short-wave ultraviolet radiation into an ozone belt. In the process all the rays that
would be extremely injurious to life are tied down. The
proportion that can force its way down to earth consists
only of rays with wave lengths in the 0.003-millimeter
range. But we are exposed to these only at high altitudes—
that is, on high mountains. There they are still so powerful
that they can cause serious burns.

It has been found that the ultraviolet rays that do manage
to pass through the ozone belt to the immediate proximity
of the earth are effectively scattered by molecules of air.
The molecules or small floating particles in the air set up an
obstacle to the rays, deflecting them from their original
path. The result is a wild welter of rays, no longer in a
directed stream but shooting in at us from all sides. If we

enter an area of such scattered radiation, we become, as it were, blanketed in rays. For this reason they may have more powerful effects than ultraviolet rays. In certain circumstances, therefore, the danger of sunburn in a thin haze may be greater than in absolutely clear air, sometimes greater even than under a perfectly cloudless sky. The same is true of snow or glacier surfaces in glaring sunlight. Even if people avoid direct sunlight, they can unwittingly be burned by scattered ultraviolet rays in shady, windless nooks on high mountains, the more so as no one bothers about adequate protection in such places. How penetrating the ultraviolet rays of the sun are is shown by the fact that even when the sky is completely overcast they are weakened far less by the cloud cover than are visible light rays. Thus, the proportion of ultraviolet rays that operates even through an overcast sky is as much as fifty per cent of the quantity effective when the sky is not obscured.

What happens when we are burned by the sun? Everyone doubtless has personal experience of the milder forms of sunburn, or of sunburn caused by snow-reflected sunlight. The reddish coloration of the skin which develops in the early stages turns brown after a short while. A few days later the skin usually begins to flake off. This peeling skin is nothing but burned—i.e., destroyed—cellular skin tissue. The extent of damage to the skin depends primarily on the wave length of the ultraviolet rays. The shorter the wave length of the radiation, the "harder" it is and the more severe is the injury to the skin.

The Skin: A Filter for Ultraviolet Rays

Like all our other organs, the skin is a living part of the body. It is therefore in no sense merely a sheath, a form of packaging for the muscle system, the tissue, the veins, and the nerves; on the contrary, through the medium of the

delicate and sensitive nerve cells situated in the skin, it conveys to the regulating center—the cortex of the brain—
news of all stimuli affecting the body from outside. It may
therefore be compared with an extremely efficient radar
screen of large area which receives and registers wave
lengths of all types, such as light and heat. It feels cold, re-
sponds to pressure and pain, excretes perspiration, stretches,
and contracts. In addition, it shares the body's breathing
functions with the lungs. The importance of skin-breathing
is shown by the fact that if two thirds of a man's skin is
burned, he is beyond human aid. Breathing through the
skin causes steady vaporization of sweat in tiny quantities,
and excess heat is thereby removed from the body.

The horny layer of our skin, which is about 1/1,000 inch
thick, consists of scaly cells without nuclei. It transmits only
about twenty per cent of the ultraviolet rays with a wave
length of less than 0.000300 millimeters. Of the rays in the
range between 0.000300 and 0.000390 millimeters, on the
other hand, up to eighty per cent get through. The entire
outer skin (the epidermis)—consisting of the horny layer
(*stratum corneum*), the clear layer (*stratum lucidum*), and
the reproductive layer (*stratum germinativum*)—causes a
twenty-per-cent weakening of the rays. Ultraviolet rays
undergo the greatest absorption in the papillary layer, the
layer in which the nerves end. Ultraviolet rays of the ordinary wave lengths do not penetrate the skin beyond this
papillary layer. This means that the rays do not get farther
than one fiftieth of an inch through the one-twelfth-inch
thickness of the human skin. The slight penetration is explained by the fact that when the ultraviolet rays reach the
papillary layer of the skin, they immediately become active
participants in chemical processes and are thereby destroyed.

The natural consequence of a sunbath in strong sunlight
is, as I have said, a reddening of the skin. This is not an effect
of visible light, and even the infrared rays are involved only
to a small extent. It is chiefly the work of ultraviolet rays.

Moreover, the reddening of the skin is not by any means an entirely "healthy" phenomenon: it is a straightforward inflammation of the skin. This inflammation resulting from sunburn is presumably caused by decomposition of nucleic acid—protein substances present in the cell nucleus—in the skin tissue. It has been shown experimentally that the active substance *histidine* is transformed by ultraviolet rays with wave lengths below 0.000270 millimeters into *histamine*, a hormone produced in tissue. Histamine is found generally in allergic conditions that affect many people whose bodies are abnormally sensitive to pollen, wool, feathers, certain flowers, and so on. In all these cases the reaction is skin irritation, or a skin rash, or reddening and swelling of the skin, or watering and inflammation of the eyes. Along with other agencies, histamine always has a hand in the game. Well known among its properties is the ability to dilate the blood vessels of the skin. The outward effect of the increased circulation in the skin thus stimulated is a reddening.

What, then, is the function performed by histamine in connection with sunburn? In the normal course of events the human body does not come into contact at all with the ultraviolet rays responsible for the formation of histamine from histidine. Normally, it is not wave lengths of 0.000270 millimeters that cause sunburn, but those of 0.000300 millimeters and above. These ultraviolet rays with longer wave lengths pass through the horny layer of the skin without any substantial loss of strength, but are not capable of taking part in the formation of histamine. If, then, the reddening of the skin can really be caused by histamine only, it is reasonable to ask where this comes from.

The ultraviolet rays destroy the nucleic acid inside the cell, releasing a fairly large quantity of histamine. It is this that floods the skin with waste products, even when ultraviolet rays with longer wave lengths are operating. Added to this is the fact that while the nucleic acid is being broken down, the cells too are flooded with waste products. These distend the cell walls till they burst, and are responsible for the formation of the painful blisters that are symptomatic of severe burns. Fever, associated with shivering fits, is the result of what is, in effect, a poisoning of the cells. In exceptional cases—specifically, where two thirds of the skin surface is burned—death may result.

In harmless cases the reddening of the skin is followed by a brown tan that lasts for varying lengths of time. This coloration is caused by the pigment granules that, under the influence of the ultraviolet radiation, form between the reproductive and papillary layers of the skin. When, after eight to ten days, the coloration of the skin has reached a point at which the blood vessels can be dilated no further, the pigment granules inside the skin rise to the top and fade. This restores the pallor of the skin, and the "healthy" color is gone. Pigmentation of the skin is mainly caused by ultraviolet rays with a wave length of less than 0.000310 millimeters. A tan may be produced without prior reddening of the skin if the skin is exposed only to ultraviolet rays with a wave length between 0.000310 and 0.000390 millimeters. A tan created by these long-wave ultraviolet rays is more lasting and finer in color.

People are not all uniformly sensitive to ultraviolet rays. As a rule, a blond person shows a stronger reaction than a person with black hair; but even among fair people there are variations. The very fair and the redheads are more than twice as sensitive as those with the darker shades of blond hair. Age, too, and the general physical constitution play equally decisive parts.

Artificial Ultraviolet Light

In 1895 a Danish engineer named Magensen was suffering from a nasty case of tetter that hideously disfigured his face.

Cypress Gardens, Florida. The same scene photographed with infrared film.

[*photographs:* PHILIP GENDREAU]

Commuters waiting for a bus at Neuilly, near Paris, are kept warm by infrared heat rays from this double-duty traffic light. [WIDE WORLD PHOTO]

A solar house at Scottsdale, Pennsylvania. Its louver contains water pipes heated by the sun. [WIDE WORLD PHOTO]

Partial view of ZETA (Zero Energy Thermonuclear Assembly).
[© U.K. Atomic Energy Authority]

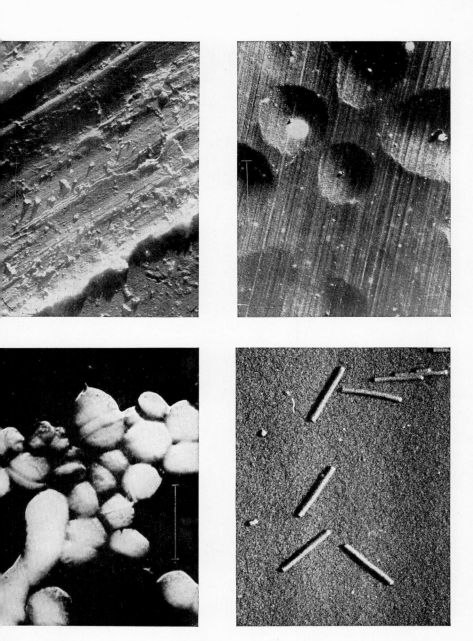

Electron-microscope photographs. *Upper left:* The surface of a used roller bearing, plated with a thin coat of chromium. *Upper right:* A polished diamond face, plated by Robley C. Williams. *Lower left:* The grotesque shapes of chromium-shadowed *staphylococcus aureus*, the bacterium that causes boils. *Lower right:* Uranium-plated tobacco-mosaic virus, previously seen only as a vague bit of straw. [*courtesy of* ROBLEY C. WILLIAMS, VIRUS LABORATORY, UNIVERSITY OF CALIFORNIA, BERKELEY]

Where X rays were discovered: Wilhelm Conrad Röntgen's laboratory in Würzburg, Germany. [WIDE WORLD PHOTO]

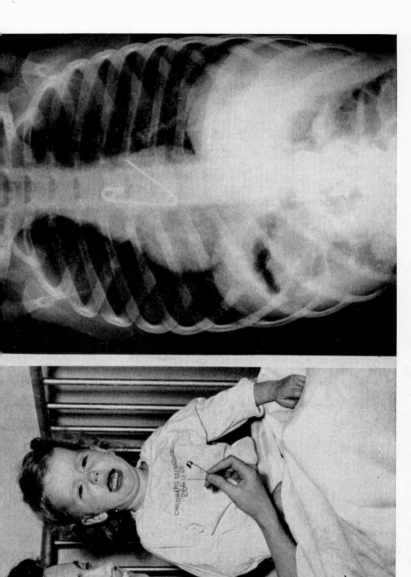

Right: An X-ray print showing a safety pin lodged in the esophagus of a 21-month-old child. *Left:* The pin held by the nurse is about the same size as the one removed. [WIDE WORLD PHOTO]

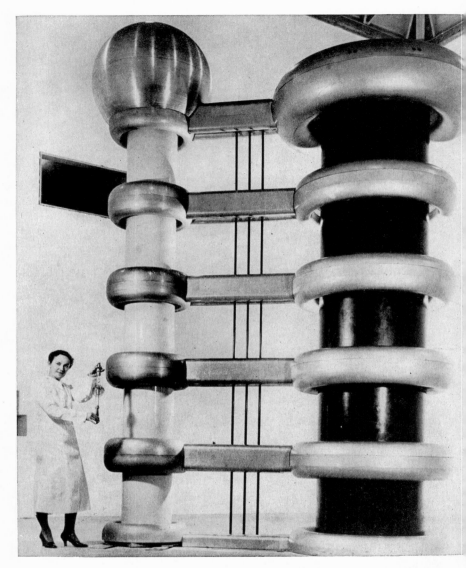

Giant X-ray tube and transformer at the Los Angeles Institute of Radiology, the newest and most powerful weapon in the war on cancer. By way of contrast, a nurse is shown holding a photographic X-ray tube such as is commonly used by physicians to photograph broken bones, etc. [*photograph:* PHILIP GENDREAU]

After unsuccessful consultations with a number of doctors, he finally went to see Dr. Niels Ryberg Finsen.

Finsen prescribed simple sunlight, but winter sunlight in Copenhagen was not very strong. Bent upon trying the effect of "artificial sunlight," Dr. Finsen approached the chief engineer of the Copenhagen power station and commissioned him to construct a large arc lamp.

The engineer carried out the order and built an arc lamp to carry a current of twenty-five amperes. The light was bright enough, but, above all, it was rich in ultraviolet rays —and these were the object of Finsen's interest.

From November to March, Magensen went to the power station daily and sat in the light of the arc lamp, which was screened by sheets of blue glass. What nobody had thought possible happened. At the end of a month the eruptions began to heal. By March, Magensen was cured of a disease described as incurable by all the other doctors who had treated him.

The case excited great attention. Two manufacturers came forward with an offer of money to enable the doctor and the power-station engineer to construct an artificial sunlight unit of their own; and in due course the first ultraviolet-radiation center in the world was set up in the garden of the Copenhagen City Hospital.

However, the new method of treatment did not work out as anticipated. It seemed as if the Magensen case had been a flash in the pan. Finsen experimented with various kinds of glass as filters for the arc lamp. He also tried glass lenses to concentrate the rays, but the patients could not stand the great heat for long. Finally, he hit upon the idea of using quartz glass. He had found that, in contrast to other kinds of glass, it transmitted ultraviolet rays well. He placed quartz-glass cuvettes, flat quartz vessels, on his patients' inflammations and eruptions, running water through the cuvettes for cooling purposes. From that day, success followed success until his own life span ran out. When he was awarded the Nobel Prize for his researches in the summer of 1904, he received it mortally ill in a wheel-chair.

The most important source of ultraviolet rays, the mercury-vapor lamp, had already been invented in 1892. In this lamp the arc is not produced in air, as in the case of the conventional arc lamp, but in an enclosed receptacle. Originally, these receptacles were made of ordinary glass, but this had its disadvantages because a large proportion of ultraviolet rays, particularly the biologically effective ones with short wave lengths, are absorbed by glass. Up to 1906 no way had been found of blowing tubes from quartz. The process for fusing quartz into transparent pieces was originated by Richard Küch, a physicist of Hanau in Germany. Subsequently the Hanauer Quartzlampengesellschaft became the first company to exploit Küch's discovery and apply his process in the manufacture of the first practical ultraviolet lamps, which are capable of generating short-wave ultraviolet rays as well as others.

The basic principle of these lamps is a very simple one. They consist of a quartz tube with a terminal at both ends. Short wires fused into the sockets connect these to *cold* electrodes made of iron. They are described as "cold" be-cause, in contrast to those in an incandescent lamp, they do not get hot. Enclosed in the tube are a minute quantity of an inert gas and a few beads of mercury. The mercury is particularly suitable for the purpose because even at room temperature it develops a marked vapor pressure, a property that enables it to be electrically excited—that is, made to glow—at such a temperature. This is achieved by applying voltage between the electrodes. The relatively weak cur-rent that passes through the tube is sufficient to excite the electrons in the outer shell of the mercury atom. What re-sults is not so much visible as invisible, ultraviolet light. When resonance vibrations are set up in the atoms, radiation with a wave length of 0.000254 millimeters is emitted which is characteristic of mercury. As already pointed out, only a small proportion of this radiation falls into the visible blue and green zones of the light spectrum. It is this radiation which gives the discharge its characteristic bluish-green color. In this process the inert gas in the tube merely acts as the medium by which energy is conveyed to the mercury atoms.

However, these short wave lengths of ultraviolet light cannot always be used. It is often necessary to employ longer ones. These can be obtained by increasing the loading of the tube, the effect of which is to shift the radiated energy into the range of long-wave ultraviolet rays. The waves now emitted are not 0.000254 millimeters in length, but something between 0.000350 to 0.000390 millimeters. The maximum wave length of these rays is in the neighborhood of 0.000380 millimeters.

Requests are sometimes made for the visible element of the radiation to be filtered out, and from time to time a particular wave length has to be suppressed. Here, ray filters come into play. If only a slight weakening of the ultraviolet rays is wanted, the agent mainly used is phosphate glass. For technical and medical purposes, good results have been obtained with *Schott's clear uviol glass*. For ultraviolet lamps used for analytical purposes, filters are inserted which are made of dark ultraviolet glass by which the spectrum line of the 0.000366-millimeter wave length is almost entirely absorbed. If wave lengths above the 0.000-310-millimeter range are required, ordinary Thuringian window glass is adequate as a filter. It has the property of absorbing waves in the range below 0.000310 millimeters. This is the reason why we are never burned by the sun in a room with closed windows, even at high altitudes.

A Weapon against Bacteria

In every cubic millimeter of air there is room for a million bacteria. But bacterial density drops as altitude above sea level increases, and for this reason the air at great heights is virtually free of bacteria. In the area of Mont Blanc, for example, we find no more than four to eleven bacteria per cubic millimeter which are noxious to human beings. The air over the Sahara and over the South American cordilleras is also said to be free of bacteria. Zones without bacteria are always formed at high altitudes or in desert areas where the ultraviolet radiation from the sun is very strong or, alternatively, where conditions in which bacteria can flourish do not exist owing to the absence of suitable breeding media.

The vital functions of micro-organisms are paralyzed by ultraviolet rays with very short wave lengths. These rays rob bacteria of the ability to propagate, and thus the clouds of bacteria in which we constantly live are considerably thinned out. It is impossible to make a close estimate of the number of bacteria and micro-organisms that are killed or hampered in their activity, but it can be said that without the secondary protection of these rays we should long since have been stifled by the bacteria around us.

Bacteria have a relatively brief generation time. With many of them, division often takes no longer than twenty to thirty minutes.

In order that bacteria may never be able to multiply on a gigantic scale, nature has confronted them with potent enemies. If this were not the case, all organic life on earth would long since have become extinct. One of these enemies, as we now know, is ultraviolet radiation. Every day when the first ray of sunlight becomes visible in the east, the great slaughter of bacteria begins afresh, and as soon as the sun sinks below the horizon, it slackens off.

In the fight against bacteria, spores, and germs in inte-

riors, sunlight is nowadays extensively replaced by modern
sources of ultraviolet light. With the correct dosage of radiation and appropriate disposition of the lamps in the space
concerned, very nearly 100-per-cent sterilization is
achieved.

If a culture of bacteria is bombarded with ultraviolet
rays, they damage not so much the protein structure as
certain specific minute parts of cells. They constitute a particular threat to the so-called control center of the cell.
This consists of a number of large molecules that govern
the other parts of the cell according to quite definite laws.
Without these large molecules there would be no growth,
no cell division, no reproduction. The vitality of the cell
depends to a very great extent on the functioning of this
control center. Modification or destruction of part of the
cell outside the control center may be caused by a dose of
ultraviolet light so strong that it paralyzes the entire chemistry of the cell; nevertheless, the moment the radiation is
stopped, the cell recovers with amazing rapidity. But if the
control center itself is hit by a single ultraviolet ray, this
is enough to kill the cell at once.

The possibility of killing bacteria and germs with ultraviolet rays has for some time been turned to good account.
Nowadays, wherever work in highly sterile conditions is
called for, ultraviolet lamps are set up for disinfection purposes. This applies particularly to the pharmaceutical industry, and more especially to rooms in which high-grade,
delicate medicines are packaged. This method is, for instance, the only means of ensuring completely sterile treatment of ampoules that are being filled with penicillin. The
procedure adopted is either to irradiate the entire room, or
to pass the ampoule-carrier through a tunnel in which the
ampoules are exposed to strong ultraviolet radiation. In
other branches of the pharmaceutical industry, such as cat-
gut processing, radiation chambers are used in which the
gut can be handled without risk of infection.

Other important fields of application for space sterilization by ultraviolet rays are premises in which foodstuffs are stored, processed, or packed. This is of special significance to dairies and the whole range of dairy products. We should not lose sight of the fact that every time milk runs into a milking pail, a quantity of bacteria goes in with it.

On the average, there are 10,000 to 20,000 bacteria in a teaspoonful of milk. By the time milk reaches a railroad station an hour after leaving a farm, the number has increased tenfold. Eight hours later, say, when it gets to the market, the milk contains half a million bacteria, and a few hours after that, ten million. In butter the number of bacteria is ten times as great. As for cheese, half its dry volume consists of living micro-organisms: rod-shaped bacilli, others with spherical shapes called cocci, corkscrew-shaped unicellular organisms called spirilla, and short bacteria in the form of a comma with whip-like movements, the vibriones. Not all of these are harmless or useful, so that in the dairy industry cleanliness is the first commandment. Consequently, the aim of all sound dairy practice is to keep the germ content of milk as low as possible. Above all, the air surrounding the milk refrigerators is kept sterile, any water used is sterilized, and efforts are made to cleanse the milk itself of bacteria.

We are now aware that this measure is a double-edged sword, because by sterilizing milk we kill not merely the harmful germs and bacteria but also all those which are of importance to us, among them the ones that produce essential vitamins in the stomach and intestines.

Ultraviolet lamps are used in cheese-making and cheese-processing plants as well as preserve factories to prevent the formation of mold. In packing and storage rooms at meat, sausage, and fish canneries, ultraviolet radiation makes a vital contribution to the keeping qualities of the foodstuffs treated—it prevents or retards bacterial infection on the surface of the goods. In breweries special care is taken to disinfect rooms where sterile beer is bottled. Sterilized water is used for washing yeast and vats.

A healthy person is immune to most bacteria and germs in the air he breathes, but this is not true of sick men or patients under anesthetic. Their resistance to disease germs is materially lowered, and they fall victim to infections much more readily than a person in good health. It is therefore extremely important to ensure that this additional source of danger to sick people is completely eliminated. The first attempt to install ultraviolet-sterilization equipment in operating rooms in Germany was made in 1952 at the district hospital at Prien am Chiemsee, Bavaria.* The appliances used were two ultraviolet-ray lamps built into the ceiling; and it was shown that sterilization of almost 100-per-cent efficacy can be achieved if the equipment is in action about two hours before surgery begins.

"*Magic*" *Effects*

Things which in normal light are in no way distinguishable from one another sometimes show perceptible differences in ultraviolet light. To some extent they assume different colors, or they take on other contours, according to the fluorescent substances they contain. Textile fibers of animal origin show a bluish to blue-violet fluorescence, while materials made of vegetable fibers give off a yellow light. Individual types of artificial silk and paper can be accurately differentiated solely by the variations in the color of their fluorescence.

In the direct light of a quartz lamp the bare skin has a deathly, greenish-violet pallor; but if an ultraviolet filter is placed in front of the source of radiation, the picture is quite a different one. Normal skin now shows a bluish-white fluorescence. When the face is exposed to these rays, the striking result in most people is to disclose a great many

* In America, the first regularly used equipment of this type dates back to about 1935, when Dr. Deryl Hart inaugurated this technique at the Duke University Hospital.

pigment spots in the middle section. The same thing happens in other parts of the body. In normal light the spots are usually not evident at all. Altogether, in filtered ultraviolet light the face appears much aged and, frequently, ugly. This fact serves the dermatologist when he uses the rays in diagnosis of skin diseases. When the skin is irradiated, a very sharp line of demarcation becomes visible between zones affected by disease and areas of healthy tissue. Examination of the human skin for fluorescent effects is consequently a valuable procedure in the study and recognition of skin diseases. The method is applied, above all, in the case of skin injuries arising from occupational diseases. Another valuable piece of knowledge for the diagnostician is the fact that skin diseases caused by fungi can be clearly recognized by reason of a special fluorescence. Under this kind of examination the smallest centers of disease can be detected. In filtered ultraviolet light our fingernails shine with a strong whitish glow, and the white fluorescence of the teeth is still more intense. However, this is true only of natural teeth: false teeth show up as dark gaps.

Bones fluoresce with a white or yellowish-white light, but only if they have not previously been exposed to strong heat. This information is of great value to archaeologists. Not infrequently in the course of excavations, bone remains are found which cannot be identified with certainty as belonging to a person who was buried or cremated; but this knowledge is often of extreme importance in the interpretation of the finds. Where prehistoric burial mounds have been uncovered, it has been shown that interred bones that have not been attacked by fire continue to fluoresce even when several thousand years old. On the other hand, bones that have been exposed to great heat are robbed almost at once of their ability to glow in filtered ultraviolet light.

Under this light the internal organs display various colors. The cortex of the brain appears yellow; the brain tissue, white in normal light, acquires a pink shade. The thyroid gland gives off a grayish-pink light, the pancreas brownish-yellow, while a cross-section of the liver shows a yellowish-green to brownish-yellow tinge. The skeletal muscles do not fluoresce and therefore stay dark.

If plants are observed in ultraviolet light the effects are at first somewhat disappointing. The miracle of weirdly luminous colors does not occur. Green leaves appear olive-green to chocolate in color. If the outer skin of the leaves is removed, the result is quite different: a glowing, carmine red. Mosses look particularly interesting in ultraviolet light. They, like algae, display a red—mostly dull red—fluorescence. This knowledge can be of great assistance to the geologist because it enables him, for instance, to demonstrate the presence in calcareous tufa of the remains of plants that caused the formation of tufa. The various lichens present a particularly gay picture when analyzed under a quartz lamp. A great variety of color tones, most of them rich, are observed, ranging from bluish-green through yellow and gleaming orange to red, according to the type of lichen concerned. To the botanist this means a considerable easing of his task of recognition and classification. If a longitudinal section cut from a branch of a horse chestnut is exposed to ultraviolet rays, the section surface shows fluorescence of an intense light blue and greenish-blue color. The substance that produces the light blue fluorescence continues to show up even when diluted in a solution of 0.0000001 grams per cubic centimeter. Oat germs sprouting in the dark glow with an intense blue color under ultraviolet light.

In the Crime Laboratory [1]

Scrutiny of documents under an ordinary ultraviolet lamp will decide whether they are authentic or "phony."

[1] See also p. 71.

Suppose the investigator starts off with the paper; in practice, no two kinds of paper fluoresce in the same way. Now, of course, the paper may be authentic and the print forged, or possibly the print is genuine and only the signature is spurious. It would be a very great coincidence if the forger happened to use the same ink as the person supposed to have signed the document, but let us assume that he has in fact come into possession of some ink of the same kind. In that case, the age of the signature will be scrutinized; an old ink will always fluoresce somewhat differently from a specimen of the same type which has been used recently.

Every trace of an erasure is immediately visible in ultraviolet light. So is every trace of a forger's having washed away the original ink with some chemical. The area around the writing will show a fuzzy fluorescence of a different shade. Nowadays writing that has been washed away or erased can be made clearly legible again.

In all such examinations use is made of various filters that suppress this or that wave length of ultraviolet light or emphasize another. The object under study is thus inspected layer by layer. Something that is concealed on the top level may be brought to light in the layer underneath. By this method all the stages of the various methods of forgery can be clearly exposed, and the criminologist can follow the working procedures of the forger step by step.

In the examination of old paintings, scrutiny of the so-called supporting structure is an important factor, and inspection in ultraviolet light shows up fakes clearly. This is particularly true where the forger has worked with aniline colors or other colors the date of whose discovery is known.

The master forger will mix his colors in accordance with the old formulas; if a formula is no longer known, he will even scrape the color off genuine old paintings and re-mix them for the brush in accordance with the old procedure, using the solvents favored at the time. He also may make use of an old painting of inferior value, carefully scraping the canvas clean. But after he has gone to all that trouble, ultraviolet light may still reveal his fraud—for instance, through the absence of those microscopically fine hair cracks that any picture develops in the course of centuries.

But ultraviolet rays have not merely proved valuable in detecting frauds; they also are in many cases indispensable to the work of the modern restorer. Old paintings often become so darkened that only hints of their contours are left. Ultraviolet rays have the capacity to conjure up a painting's original beauty once more; in many cases, a restoration cannot be carried out without their assistance.

In the same way, many a faded old manuscript becomes legible again under ultraviolet light. It is particularly effective in the case of palimpsests—parchments or the like from which writing has been erased partially or completely (in some instances, twice or three times) to make room for a new text. By the use of ultraviolet rays with appropriate filters it is possible to read the texts underneath layer by layer. In cases of parchments from which only certain passages of the text were erased so that other passages could be substituted, ultraviolet rays have exposed a number of historical forgeries; at times two versions of the same occurrence have come to light, one of them obviously written decades after the original.

Microscopy by Fluorescence

Limitations are imposed on the ordinary light microscope by the wave length of light; but the range can be extended if microscopes are built to function with ultraviolet rays, which have shorter wave lengths. Microscopes of this kind have disadvantages: the object to be observed can no longer be viewed directly by the eye, but must be approached by way of a photographic plate. An object is therefore not visible to us until it has been photographed. Nevertheless, the resolving power of a microscope can be materially extended by this method. ("Resolving power" means an optical instrument's ability to form distinguishable images of individual objects. It may be noted here that the shorter the wave length of the rays used to produce the image, the greater is the resolving power.)

The fluorescent microscope utilizes ultraviolet rays as a "light source." Microscopic preparations are illuminated with filtered ultraviolet light.

Naturally, the lenses of a microscope of this kind must not themselves be fluorescent, any more than the cover glass or slide. In addition, they must readily transmit the filtered ultraviolet light.

Fluorescent microscopy is also feasible with an ordinary microscope. All that is needed is a filter to intercept the ultraviolet rays before they reach the eye. This measure is necessary to prevent any possible injury to the eye. Without a filter, moreover, the observer would see the microscopic picture through a bright fog of light, as it were, and would not be able to make out any of the details of the object.

Normally, when we examine unstained microscopic sections of animal and vegetable organs in filtered ultraviolet light, only slight differences are noticeable. The color shading is fairly uniform, ranging from gray to brownish-lilac. More differences are brought out if preparations— of bacteria, for example—are stained red or blue; but even then the preparation may not stand out sharply enough against the background in the otherwise colorless and brightly lit microscopic field of vision. Observation by fluorescent microscope avoids this. In the field of vision encountered here, which is slightly grayish-violet in tone but otherwise dark, each individual bacterium stands out bathed in yellow light. This makes it impossible for bacterial smear preparations to be erroneously judged free of germs. Moreover, the fluorescent microscope does not even require a quartz lamp as a source of radiation. Visible light is sometimes sufficient because, like ultraviolet light, it stimulates luminescence in certain materials. The best method is to use a powerful low-voltage lamp with a blue filter in front of it. If an additional blue filter is attached to the eyepiece of the microscope, the gleaming yellow bacteria appear on a pitch-black background.

CHAPTER 4

From "Magic" Light to Fluorescent Lamp

THE NIGHT before Columbus was to set foot on the territory of the New World, he perceived and pointed out lights ahead. There was agreement that these lights must be human signals, and it was conjectured that people ashore must in some mysterious fashion have been apprised of the approach of the galleons. The following day, October 12, 1492, the voyagers sighted land. Columbus took it to be India.

He was in error on both counts. The land was not the India he was seeking, and the lights he had sighted had not been lit by human hands. They had been produced by myriads of glowing marine worms that come up to the surface during the last quarter of the moon, particularly on autumn nights. As Columbus's men had been clamoring for the ships to be turned back, and in fact had been on the verge of mutiny, these marine worms may be said to have saved his life—even, we may suppose, the lives of all the ships' companies, for turning about with mutinous crews would have meant, in effect, the end of all on board.

"Phantom Ships"

Again and again sailors have been deluded and frequently terrified by "magical lights" and luminous surfaces at sea. Many are the tales, especially from tropical waters, of nights when huge areas of the sea were lit up by a magic luster. The sides of ships passing through such areas became luminous; and at times clouds of spray from a stormy sea would leave the keel or even the standing sails gleaming with light. Such phenomena lent the ships a ghostly air. We know now that vast stretches of the sea can be made spontaneously luminescent by the presence of countless numbers of cystoflagellata, each about the size of a pin. On dark nights, of course, their luminosity can be particularly striking.

In the late hours of July 11, 1879, the British training ship H.M.S. *Bacchante* was on a voyage to the West Indies with the future King George V on board as a naval cadet. Suddenly, about 200 yards from the ship on the starboard side, a mysterious-looking brig hove in sight. She was bathed in a reddish-yellow glow, but otherwise carried no lights. For several seconds she stood out clearly in the darkness of the stormy night—and then was gone. At that moment, through sheer terror, the lookout up on the mast must have lost his balance, for almost the instant the apparition was sighted, he came crashing down onto the ship's planks and broke his neck. In all probability this brig was lit up by cystoflagellata on its sides, which an oncoming wave may have washed clean again.

"Witches' Meat" and "Luminous Fleas"

Luminescent bacteria are a special kind of biological light-emitters. They are sometimes found on meat in slaughterhouses and market halls—in fact, wherever meat is regularly stored. The color of the light given off by these bacteria varies from silvery white and yellowish-green to bluish-white, according to their location and their conditions of life. This sheen on carcass meat and dead fish was known to Aristotle.

In the Middle Ages this luminescence was sometimes explained in terms of sorcery. People spoke of "witches' meat." Its consumption, they said, would produce "grievous bodily ills and spasms." The luminescence does occur shortly before the onset of decay, and eating such meat may very well lead to meat poisoning. At Lyons in 1530 a "female person and witch" was burned at the stake because the authorities had found in her house—in a "kitchen of such foulness as the world had never seen—witches' meat" that showed glowing patches as big as thaler pieces. The glow on these patches, the chronicler continues, did not "go out" until the executioner's bell was tolled, "whereat the Devil rode out through the chimney, leaving behind in the kitchen a most abominable stench." The "witch" had confessed on the rack that she was in league with the Devil, and the authorities had had "an easy trial."

Even as late as 1672 such an enlightened spirit as Robert Boyle, the first man to distinguish between genuine and false chemical elements, found luminous meat a source of intense interest. Since Otto von Guericke had invented the air pump in 1650, it had become fashionable to put things in sealed containers and remove the air from inside. Boyle applied this procedure to glowing meat to see how the luminosity would behave in such circumstances. The more air he pumped out, the dimmer the sheen became until it finally vanished altogether. Without being aware of it, he had proved that luminescent bacteria need air—or, more precisely, oxygen—in order to give off light. What Boyle did not yet know was that the glow derives from luminescent bacteria, and that by depriving them of oxygen he had killed them.

. . .

To a person walking in the country it is a weird experience when, in the half-light of the woods, he stumbles upon
a rotting tree trunk that faintly glows against the shadowy
background. The sight of luminous half-decayed mosses is
by no means uncommon in certain Central European forests.
A small filamentous fungus, sending out this feeble greenish-yellow light, flourishes among the decomposing cellu-
lose material of that region.

Luminescent bacteria frequently occur on living animals.
This fact was once forced upon a well-known zoologist
who believed he had discovered a new type of sand flea. In
the midst of some decaying seaweed he had found sand
fleas that gave off a strange glow, and he took them to be
a type of "luminous flea." Before he proceeded to give a
Latin name to the creature, however, he had a word with a
colleague of his, who made it clear to him that the fleas he
had observed were ordinary specimens afflicted with "glowing disease."

Sand fleas searching for food among rotting vegetation
and animal corpses on the seashore not infrequently become
infected with luminescent bacteria. These find their way
into the interior of the flea's body and go on glowing there
as long as they are supplied with the necessary oxygen. On
account of the transparent character of the flea's skin, the
light from the bacteria shows through, creating the impression that the whole insect is lit up. Various forms of this
"glowing disease" have been observed in the smaller crabs
and flying insects. Owing to the constant drain of oxygen
they suffer, the creatures affected die of exhaustion.

About twenty years ago a Japanese biologist succeeded
in breeding colonies of luminescent bacteria that shone
with a pleasant yellowish-red glow. He hit upon the idea of
making these colonies the light source of a new type of
miner's lamp. A large number of pit disasters are caused
when coal dust becomes ignited by faulty or damaged

miner's lamps; the biologist's lamp would have banished that danger because, of course, the bacteria would have given off "cold light."

However, the colony of bacteria he bred did not start glowing until 74 hours had passed; the light then gained in intensity until the 180th hour, after which it maintained a constant level for about 45 hours. From that point on, the light slowly died down. For a while the blast-proof bacteria lamp aroused some interest in Japanese army circles as a device that might safely be used in powder plants.

A luminous beetle of exceptional brightness, called the *cocuje*, occurs in Brazil. The native women pin—or rather, glue—these beetles in their hair as living diamonds, so to speak.

Certain tribes of the interior of that country also use the beetles to illuminate their huts. They shut up a fairly large number of the *cocujes* in little cages, and travelers report that the light is strong enough to read by.

Not far from Waitomo, New Zealand, there is a small cave that is kept bright with the light of millions of insect larvae. The ceiling, with its innumerable tiny points of light, is said to look like a star-studded sky. These lights come from larvae of the fly *arachnocarpa luminosa*, which live in delicately spun cocoons. The larva has a luminous organ in the rear segment of its abdomen; the light it emits passes through the glassy chitin casing of the body and is gently diffused by the cocoon.

In a gland the larva secretes a sticky fluid, which it sends out in long threads; up to two dozen of these hang from each of the diminutive creatures, dangling from the grotto's ceiling for about two feet, like tiny fishing lines. When the gnats, hordes of which visit the cave regularly, blunder into the tacky threads, they are left sticking to them as if to flypaper; there they fall prey to bats. The larvae "shut off" their luminous organs at the slightest disturbance of the threads by contact. The eerie effect of the lights, which flash on and off, is enhanced by their reflection in a placid stream that flows through the cave.

The Secret of the Firefly

All of us at one time or another have asked ourselves how the light emitted by fireflies is produced. The ancient Romans spoke of "*stellae volantes*," of stars flying between heaven and earth. For a time in the Middle Ages people believed that the light of fireflies was shed by the souls of departed newborn infants who, being unbaptized, could not enter heaven. As bats are fond of hunting fireflies, it was asserted that Lucifer himself was on the prowl for these innocent souls.

Well, how *do* fireflies, without being stimulated by energy in the form of rays, manage to give off light? Normal yellow phosphorus glows only when it combines with oxygen in the air. In doing so, it is oxidized and slowly burns away. The oxygen, too, is burned in the process, but so slowly that no perceptible rise in temperature occurs. This means of creating light stands in complete contrast to the process that takes place in the luminous organ of the firefly. The phenomenon of light in fireflies of all kinds is controlled by a gland in which two substances are formed: *luciferin* and *luciferase*.

During the glowing process, intermediate products appear. These do not convert the released chemical energy into heat; on the contrary, they curb the heat. This can be done only by substances in which certain groups of molecules are electrically screened by atoms of impurities. The previously absorbed energy is not released in a burst, but is given off again gradually. That is the secret of the key substance in fireflies.

Even now, all that we know about it is that the compound consists of carbon, hydrogen, oxygen, and phosphorus. Elements such as sulfur and the halogens—substances, such as fluorine, chlorine, bromine, and iodine, which form salts with metals—are absent. If carbon, hydrogen, phosphorus, and oxygen are mixed, none of these four elements glows except phosphorus; and even phosphorus does not glow in such a way that the light can be switched on and off at will. The chemist of today is, of course, in a position to manufacture luminescent materials of good quality, some of them with luminescence of unusually long duration. However, they all need light or electrical energy to stimulate them, and they burn away, even if at a relatively slow rate.

In luminescent creatures the mere presence of oxygen is sufficient to set off the luminous effect. And how efficient the luminous organ is! Where we normally have to accept a 95-per-cent loss of energy in the case of everyday incandescent lamps, or one of 60 per cent in the case of fluorescent lamps, the firefly, with a far smaller expenditure of energy, achieves a 98-per-cent light yield. Moreover, the color of this light—yellowish-green—is precisely the one to which our eyes are most sensitive. So far, the only thing we know about the mechanism with which the firefly produces *cold* light is that the glowing process involves an enzyme, a protein substance that, though it alters chemical compounds, is not itself consumed. The American physiologist Otto Meyerhof has succeeded in exciting luciferin to glow by mixing it with adenosine triphosphate, a substance that is presumed to play a large role in the phosphorus balance of living creatures with luminous organs. Up to now no one has succeeded in preparing the light-producing substance synthetically. If we were one day to reach that point, we should be free of most of our lighting and power troubles.

Like a Great City by Night

William Beebe, the American zoologist and deep-sea explorer, and more recently Auguste Piccard, the Swiss physicist who descended to great depths in a pressure-proof bathysphere, both say in their accounts that forty per cent of all the fish they encountered during their dives were equipped with luminous organs. Beebe speaks of fish with "telescopic eyes" that can shoot in and out. Then there are fish whose "lamps" are fitted with movable reflecting lenses and obscuring devices.

One of these "light specialists" is the Banda fish, which lives off the Banda Islands in Indonesia. Its luminous organ houses luminescent bacteria in gland-like cells. The curious thing is that these cellular sacs are situated just under the eyes, a fact that lends the fish a quite startling appearance. These sacs of bacteria are mistaken for its eyes, which remain concealed in the darkness. The Banda fish can switch its bacterial lamps on and off in an instant. It possesses a black flap of skin that performs the function of a large eyelid, covering or uncovering the luminous organ according to the fish's needs.

The *anomalops* fish (the name means no more than "unusual eye") has an organ similar to that of the Banda fish, but carries the cellular bag of luminous bacteria on the inner side of a muscular hinge. If the fish closes the muscular hinge, the light is turned off; when it opens the hinge, the luminous patch reappears. Beebe reports that it is an uncanny spectacle to see several of these fish "signaling" at the same time. The rich variety of luminescent colors found in the ocean depths reminded Beebe of a distant view of a great city at night, with its many twinkling neon signs, its lighted cars and buses.

There are still other denizens of the animal kingdom to amaze us in this deep-sea world. One instance is an inkfish that, instead of squirting ink, pours out a luminous cloud.

Another representative of the inkfish family secretes a whole cloak of brilliant light. This cloak consists of many billions of minute luminescent bacteria that normally live as parasites. When danger threatens, the inkfish throws out its colony of bacteria to make itself invisible. Still another deep-sea fish observed by Beebe secretes a substance that in water becomes spontaneously luminescent. The fluid then floats about the water in the form of a glowing thread or ball or hoop, distracting pursuers or luring prey.

Stones That Glow in the Dark

In 1602, when alchemy was still in full flower, Vincentus Casciorolo, a shoemaker of Bologna who was searching for the "philosophers' stone," baked a mixture of flour and crushed heavy spar in his oven until it was red hot. After allowing the molten mass to cool, he held it up to the light for a while before putting it in a dark corner of his workshop. And suddenly he noticed that the substance he had obtained glowed in the dark. This was the first artificially prepared luminous material. It was not the "philosophers' stone," did not possess the power of transmuting base metals into gold, and did not make the cobbler a rich man— though it made him a well-known one.

The discoverer of the second luminous substance, Georg Brandt, a Hamburg merchant, did not fare much better than the shoemaker of Bologna. One day in 1668 he evaporated some human urine to dryness. The residue consisted of a golden-yellow substance that caused burns when it came into contact with the skin. Brandt did not doubt for an instant that the material he had discovered possessed highly mysterious properties. The stuff glowed at night with a bluish light. This glow aroused tremendous excitement at the time, and Brandt named his discovery "cold fire." Johann Sigismund Elsholz later named this substance *phosphorus* ("light-bringer"), the name it still bears today.

Although Brandt, who wanted to use it to make gold, kept the process secret, rumors about the mysterious chemical discovered in Hamburg reached Dresden, where it came to the ears of two alchemists, Johann Kunckel and Johann Daniel Krafft. They set out for Hamburg to learn more about it, and Kunckel managed to wrest the secret from Brandt.

Later Gottfried Wilhelm Leibniz brought the spontaneously luminous substance to the notice of the Academy of Sciences in Paris. He also submitted to the Elector of Brandenburg a plan for the manufacture of phosphorus fire bombs. The Elector was fired with enthusiasm. But where could the vast quantities of urine needed for its manufacture be obtained?

With swift resolution His Highness issued a remarkable order of the day: from now on, soldiers were not to perform their natural need in the open; large casks would be kept in the barracks for collection of the precious stuff, and a reward was offered for casks that were rapidly filled. The gallant grenadiers, fusiliers, and musketeers soon conceived the notion that the urine was used in the manufacture of gold. The rumor spread very quickly, and force was lent to it by the secrecy that surrounded the dispatch of the filled casks to a place on the Lüneburg Heath. There distilling, boiling, and brewing were in progress day and night. Leibniz, who himself directed the experiments, sustained burns again and again as he worked on the phosphorus.

Even at that time it was observed that many compounds of phosphorus emit a glow after being exposed to light for a while. Later phosphorus—of which today three forms are familiar to us: white, red, and black—became the basis of many light-storing materials that not only provided the groundwork for a new kind of light-producer, but also gave rise to a series of highly important discoveries.

By the turn of the century there was knowledge of more

than a thousand light-storing materials—substances that retain an afterglow for a while after exposure to light. How this phenomenon occurs was revealed only by modern atomic theory.

"Frozen Light"

Ultraviolet light is invisible to our eyes. It is dark light. However, if it falls on certain substances, it makes them luminescent. The wave length of the invisible light is shifted toward the long wave lengths and therefore toward the visible portion of the spectrum. For example, if zinc silicate is irradiated with ultraviolet light having a wave length of 0.000254 millimeters, the emergent light wave measures 0.000550 millimeters. We experience a light wave of this length as yellow light. If zinc sulfide is excited with ultraviolet rays having a wave length of 0.000365 millimeters, the substance glows with a green phosphorescence.

Different terms have been chosen to convey the faculties of giving off light after irradiation and during irradiation. Thus we speak of *fluorescence* when the luminescent material—for example, fluorspar, fluorescin, or petroleum —glows during exposure to ultraviolet light, but of *phosphorescence* when it continues to glow after exposure to these rays. Whereas in fluorescence the glow ceases immediately after the radiation is cut off, in the case of phosphorescence the glow takes some little time to die away. What happens in these processes? An atom can give off light only after energy is supplied to it. The result of each application of energy is a spasmodic exchange of electrons in the electron shell of the atom, in the course of which the electrons jump to higher energy levels. After a short while they fall back into their old orbit, and the energy thus released is given off.

In luminescent materials in the solid state the process is

somewhat more complicated. In ordinary substances a large proportion of the energy is always transformed into heat. This does not happen, as was demonstrated by the Heidelberg physicist Philipp Lenard, when the crystalline structure of a substance is "disturbed" by the addition of impurity atoms. The addition of copper, manganese, or lithium atoms that become active within the lattice gaps of a fluorescent or phosphorescent substance is regarded as such a disturbance. If we impart energy to such a substance by means of ultraviolet rays, for example, the electrons of certain atoms are again lifted to a higher energy level, as in normal circumstances; but owing to the screening, and hence disturbing, influence of the impurity atoms, they are no longer able to revert immediately to their original state. They do this only quite gradually and fall back by stages, so to speak, into their old places.

The radiation given off follows the same sequence: the substance in question continues to glow until all the electrons have found their way back to the energy level they previously occupied. This may take fractions of seconds, but it may also last hours, days, weeks, or months. The determining factors are the nature of the material and the kind of impurity atoms added to it. For instance, as we have already said, to render sulfides of rare earth metals phosphorescent, traces of a substance such as copper, manganese, thallium, lithium, vanadium, or bismuth are mixed with them in proportions of between 1 : 100 and 1 : 1,000,000.

German people have memories of the "blackout brooches,"[1] which were put on the market in large quantities during World War II. These brooches were found to have certain peculiarities that resulted in some interesting experiments. For instance, their luminosity diminished con-

[1] The *Verdunklungsplakette* was a device used in Germany during World War II to enable people to see one another as they moved about in blacked-out streets. It consisted of a plaque coated with phosphorescent material and worn pinned to a jacket or coat like a brooch. (Translator's note)

siderably whenever the air temperature dropped. Conversely, it rose when, as in summer, the air temperature was high. This indicated that under the influence of heat the electrons returned to their starting positions more quickly than at low temperatures. On the strength of this knowledge, an experiment was made. A luminous substance, strongly phosphorescent after exposure to light, was cooled to minus 140 degrees centigrade by means of liquid air. The result was that, practically from one second to the next, the luminosity dropped from a maximum value to zero. The substance was then taken out of the liquid air again, and after a while slowly began to glow once more. It thus became clear that light can be *frozen* and *thawed* again. This sounds very much like the story of Baron Münchhausen's famous horn that, when warmed up, would play the melody previously "frozen" by the cold. Nevertheless, the experiment with liquid air is anything but a piece of Münchhauseniana.

"Cold" Light Instead of Hot

On October 21, 1879, Thomas Alva Edison, after expending more than $40,000 in fruitless experiments, succeeded in making an incandescent lamp in which a loop of carbonized cotton thread glowed in a vacuum. Later Edison recalled how he and his collaborators sat there that night watching the lamp burn without going out, and how their delight grew the longer the lamp burned. The magic radiated by the carbonized cotton thread so lengthened their day that no one thought of sleep even after twenty hours.

Edison was at that time ignorant of the experiments of a German immigrant, Heinrich Goebel, about twenty-five years earlier. This man had evacuated small bottles and turned them into incandescent lamps by inserting charred bamboo fibers. He had sometimes used these lamps to illuminate his home, and had also attached one of them to the pushcart with which he eked out a living in his neighborhood. Apparently the world had passed by his invention heedlessly.

Thomas Alva Edison realized right away that electric light would be economical only if used in conjunction with a cheap source of power. Werner von Siemens, a former German artillery officer, had already invented such a source —the dynamo. This machine provided engineers with a means of producing electric current of unlimited strength cheaply and simply. Cheap power and cheap electric lamps were just what Edison had pictured. But the theory was easier than the performance; the price of Edison's first incandescent lamps was a dollar and ten cents.

His contemporaries, particularly the producers of kerosene and kerosene lamps, the carbide manufacturers, and the candlemakers, predicted that there was no future for the Edison lamp, that electric light could never supplant gas, the oil lamp, or the candle. A dollar ten *was* a lot of money for a lamp, and Edison knew it. He began to sell the lamps for forty cents a piece. At first this meant an outright loss, but only until Edison was in a position to lower the manufacturing cost to twenty-two cents. He kept on selling at forty cents and soon made good the initial loss.

In 1881, two years after the first incandescent bulb left Edison's workshop, the steamship *Columbia* was fitted with a thousand of them. Within another two years there were 357 electric-power stations in existence, feeding over 70,-000 incandescent lamps, each with an average life of 100 hours.

The electric bulbs devised by Edison (and, independently, by Sir Joseph Wilson Swan) were carbon-filament lamps. Their light yield was a maximum of three lumens per watt of electric power supplied—i.e., the approximate amount of light given off by three candles in a second. By 1898 the light yield had been doubled.

In 1902 the Austrian Carl Auer von Welsbach succeeded in drawing osmium, a metal with a very high melting point, into fine wire. The *osmium lamp* had a light yield of seven lumens per watt, but it failed to catch on because its filaments were too brittle, a fact that severely limited the life of the lamps. A search was therefore made for another filament material. By way of tantalum, the choice finally fell in 1905 on tungsten. Having a very high melting point (3,380 degrees centigrade), this metal turned out to be excellent material for filaments. However, the durability of the filaments, which were first obtained by a spray process, continued to be unsatisfactory until a change was brought about by the *sintering process*. By this we mean fusing separate grains of metal by heating. The sintered metal is obtained from loose metal powder to which a light base metal is added: the mixture is molded under high pressure, and is subsequently heated to a temperature just below the melting point of the principal metal. Raw material prepared in this way is then drawn in special draw plates, a procedure with which it later proved possible to manufacture filaments as fine as one two-thousandth of an inch in diameter. Filaments such as this carried a load beyond that of any previous type of lamp. The light yield now climbed to eight lumens per watt. Finally, in 1916, the spiral-filament tungsten lamp brought an increase to nine lumens per watt. The incandescent spiral was manufactured by winding the fine filament on a thin core. Nevertheless, this kind of lamp had the disadvantage of high heat loss. From 1932 onward this was cut down by doubling the spiral and filling the lamp with krypton, one of the inert gases. Krypton is a poorer conductor of heat than the argon used in tungsten lamps up to that time. With this double-spiral lamp a light yield of thirteen lumens was attained. Except in the case of certain special lamps, that figure still holds.

As long as seventy years ago Samuel Pierpont Langley, the physicist, criticized the low efficiency of incandescent electric lamps. He pointed out that 99 per cent of the energy supplied was transformed into useless heat. "With these electric lamps," he wrote, "we heat the room more than we illuminate it." Langley was right. There has not been much change in this state of affairs to this day. Even in the most modern types of electric bulb, ninety-one to ninety-five per cent of the energy supplied takes the form of heat radiation, and only between five and nine per cent appears as light. How, then, could the efficiency of the lamps be raised? We should have to heat the filament to between 6,000 and 7,000 degrees centigrade; but even the most heat-resistant metal does not stand up to a temperature of this magnitude. Tungsten melts at 3,380 degrees centigrade and the other metals much sooner. That is why our everyday electric bulb does not give off white daylight: the major part of its radiation lies in the red portion of the spectrum. Lighting engineers have found no way of boosting the light yield above nine per cent by using heated solids as light sources.

A quite different lighting technique has been built up on the basis of the gas-discharge tube invented by Heinrich Geissler, a mid-nineteenth-century German glassblower and mechanic who worked for many years as a laboratory assistant to Julius Pflücker at Bonn. He was skilled in the art of blowing twisted glass tubes from which he evacuated air. When he fused metal electrodes into the tubes and applied a high voltage between them, a feeble sea-green light was produced. The light emitted was *cold*, not hot. This simple tube brought a series of inventions and discoveries in its train. Through its agency, cathode rays were discovered, which in turn led to the discovery of the electron. The same apparatus, somewhat modified, provided the basis for the first X-ray tube. Lastly, it brought about the invention of the cathode-ray tube, the Braun tube, and the neon glow tube.

In 1900 the American D. Macfarlan Moore reached the important conclusion that the glow produced in Geissler tubes originates from gases and vapors as soon as these are acted upon by an electric field. Ever since a method of obtaining liquid air had been found, suitable gases such as neon, helium, and argon had been available in sufficient quantity. The first neon tubes were now constructed. Although their light did not lend itself to room illumination, it was excellent for publicity purposes, and the triumphal progress of the illuminated advertisement began.

The neon tube was but one step on the way to a new type of illumination which finally led to the fluorescent lamp. This lamp makes use of an effect that has been known for a long time. If luminescent substances are irradiated with invisible ultraviolet light, they *transform* the short-wave invisible light into long-wave visible light. The first step in this direction was taken when a glass screen treated with luminescent substances was moved in front of a mercury-vapor lamp giving off a sufficient quantity of ultraviolet radiation. As soon as the screen was hit by ultraviolet rays, it began to glow. The glow vanished when the screen was moved out of range of the rays. When separated from each other, neither the tube nor the screen glowed. In the practical application of this principle, the detached luminescent screen was automatically abandoned when it was found that the necessary luminescent materials—silicate phosphors, such as zinc silicate, or sulfide phosphors, such as zinc sulfide, with their yellowish fluorescence—could just as easily be deposited by vaporization on the inner walls of an ultraviolet-ray tube. Be that as it might, the cold, pallid light at first failed to win approval.

After the first tests with fluorescent lamps there was

general agreement that a serviceable form of light would not be achieved by the use of a single luminescent substance. Attempts were made to obtain a more pleasant light by mixing various fluorescent materials. Some experience had already been accumulated in the manufacture of fluorescent screens for television tubes. The most appropriate effect for living rooms was achieved by mixing luminescent colors that blended into a pink shade of light, while for factory interiors and business premises it resulted from tones that produced white daylight.

The luminescent materials to which increased attention was subsequently devoted usually have a crystalline structure. They are thus mostly available for processing in the form of a white powder. The color of the light emitted can be predetermined by the addition of traces of special impurity elements—for the most part, heavy metals. If, for example, a few copper atoms are incorporated in the crystal lattice of zinc sulfide, the shade of luminescence will be green; if silver atoms are introduced, it will be blue. The essential condition for quality in a luminescent substance is the highest possible degree of purity in the bulk material. Impurities to the amount of only one gram in ten tons cannot be permitted because they produce an appreciably poorer light yield. The proportion of impurity must be less than $1:1,000,000$.

When luminescent substances for use with luminescent tubes are mixed, care has to be taken that the individual active substances have the correct duration of afterglow. By this we mean the continuing glow of a luminescent substance after excitation has ceased. The duration of afterglow must at least be long enough for the so-called *dark intervals*, arising from the use of alternating current, to be bridged as efficaciously as possible. This is the only way to avoid "flicker" in the lamps. Nowadays the procedure of applying luminescent materials to the inside walls of fluorescent tubes is avoided altogether. Instead, the tubes are made of glass with which the phosphors are mixed in the molten state. A non-fluorescent scattering material is added to promote diffusion of the ultraviolet rays when they penetrate the glass, a device by which the luminosity is enhanced. Technicians can now produce luminescent glass adapted to the most varied ranges of the light spectrum.

Fluorescent tubes now provide a source of light with a relatively high light yield, lower flux density, and less dazzle, and with a wide range of choice in colors. In the case of a 24-inch fluorescent tube, the light yield at present obtainable stands at 30 to 40 lumens per watt for the white, bluish-white, and reddish-white tones, 40 to 45 lumens per watt for the yellow tones, and 55 to 65 lumens per watt for the yellowish-green and green tones. If 48-inch tubes are used, the light yield goes up by about 30 per cent. By contrast, a 15- to 60-watt incandescent bulb achieves only about 8 to 12 lumens, and larger lamps (100 to 500 watts) 13.5 to 19 lumens per watt. The transformation of energy in fluorescent lamps thus produces an output of 15 to 20 per cent or more, whereas in the case of incandescent lamps the output ranges from 4.5 per cent to a maximum of 9 per cent.

CHAPTER 5

From the Cathode-Ray Tube to the Electron Microscope

THE ANCIENT GREEKS realized that when amber was rubbed, mysterious forces were produced, and they therefore ascribed a "soul" to it; the origin of these forces remained hidden from them. The electron, too, remained unknown to such early physicists of modern times as William Gilbert, Otto von Guericke, Luigi Galvani, and Alessandro Volta—indeed, even to such comparatively recent scientists as André Marie Ampère and Michael Faraday. Yet many of these men were throughout their lives concerned with electrical phenomena, whether in the course of a wide variety of experiments they produced sparks, constructed batteries, built transmission systems, or described the phenomena in detailed treatises. Even Edison was unable to identify the real carriers of electrical phenomena.

None of these scientists could possibly know that electricity was atomic in character. The current that Edison put through the filaments of his early lamps and measured more than a hundred times consisted of these tiny carriers of electricity.

It was left to the English physicist Joseph John (afterward Sir Joseph) Thomson to lift the veil shrouding the phenomenon of electricity. In 1899 he demonstrated that electrons are the carriers of electricity and, further, that each of them carries an elementary quantum of a negative electric charge. This discovery had been preceded by a series of experiments in which Julius Pflücker, Johann Wilhelm Hittorf, Sir William Crookes, Philipp Lenard, and others had taken part.

In 1869 a noteworthy paper, "The Conduction of Current in Gases," appeared in Johann Christian Poggendorff's *Annalen der Physik und Chemie*, the foremost scientific journal in Europe. It was signed by Johann Wilhelm Hittorf, professor of physics at the academy in Münster. While the academy had a good reputation, the writer's name was practically unknown in learned circles. Born in Bonn in 1824, Hittorf had obtained his doctorate at the early age of twenty-one and qualified as a university teacher shortly thereafter in his native town. Some years later he was appointed to the Münster academy.

Hittorf's article was based on investigations made by his teacher Julius Pflücker. Interested in the stratification of the colored rings that appear in Geissler tubes when a current is passed through them, Pflücker had come upon a phenomenon that led him to believe that he had discovered a new kind of radiation. It emanated, in his view, from the cathode of the tube—that is, from the point connected to the negative terminal of the voltage source. It appeared in the form of a number of feebly glowing threads of a greenish hue which often reached as far as the middle of the tube. At times, however, the threads did not put in an appearance, which made Pflücker wonder whether he was not, after all, mistaken.

Now Hittorf had gone further into the matter of these strange rays and made some interesting observations. "The faintly glowing rays," he wrote, "start from the cathode of the tube. Their trajectories are independent of the position of the electrode to which, for example, the positive pole of the battery is connected. If a piece of sheet metal with a prominent outline in the form, say, of a cross is located inside the tube, a sharp silhouette of it appears on the glass wall opposite. It has been shown, in addition, that the rays are affected by magnetic forces. The greenish threads of light can be deflected by a strong magnetic field as if they were rigid threads of current."

Was this really a new kind of ray? And, if so, what could be done with it? Could it perhaps be used for lighting purposes? Not until nearly ten years later was this strange phenomenon taken up again, this time by William (afterward Sir William) Crookes.

Radiant Matter?

A physicist and chemist, Crookes had been one of the first to follow up Bunsen's and Kirchhoff's method of detecting new elements by spectrum analysis. Using this procedure, he had in 1861 discovered the element thallium.

In 1879 Crookes reported, in a lecture before the Royal Society, that by using rarefied air and a higher voltage he had increased the efficiency of the Geissler discharge tube that Hittorf had used. This, he went on, made possible improved observation of the pencil of rays emanating from the cathode. All the indications were that the rays emitted were of a corpuscular—i.e., physical—nature. Crookes added that, though reluctant to apply the term "radiant matter" to these, he could find no better description for them.

Several years later the young German physicist Philipp Lenard at Heidelberg took a fresh look at the strange radiation discovered by Crookes. Lenard made his own tubes and himself fused in the electrodes. Once he would use iron, another time copper, or carbon, or whatever other material suitable for electrodes lay ready to hand. In all his work he was constantly bothered by the fact that he was forced to study the properties of the radiation through the glass envelope of the tube. Was there no way to get the rays out into the open?

He tried to build them an exit—a window—with every conceivable kind of glass: wafer-thin glass, colored and corrugated glass, various types of quartz glass. But the rays would not come out of the tube. He was on the point of stopping his experiments when in November 1891 Heinrich Hertz, the well-known Bonn physicist, mentioned in an article published in the *Annalen der Physik* that sheeting made of thin aluminum allowed the passage of *cathode radiation*, as he called the rays.

A year later Lenard had a tube that permitted the rays to emerge. He had had to roll out the sheet aluminum to a thickness of one twenty-five-thousandth of an inch before it would allow the rays to pass through. "The magnetic deflectability of the rays," he wrote in a paper submitted to the Prussian Academy of Sciences, "depends solely on the strength of the discharge voltage in the tube. The rays themselves are diffused in matter, turning gases into conductors of electricity and causing chemical reactions. The fact that the rays, whose particle character can scarcely be doubted any longer, are able to pass through thin metal foil leads us to infer that the ray particles must be smaller than molecules, indeed smaller than atoms. If, on the other hand, such small particles produce readily measurable quantities of heat merely by their impact on the glass wall of the tube, this argues that they must, at the same time, be moving at a high velocity."

However, it was still not known what "cathode rays" really were.

Fast Electrons

To be better able to study cathode radiation, Joseph John Thomson, head of the Cavendish Laboratory at Cambridge, constructed a completely new tube. It differed from the conventional Hittorf tube in that it ended in a long neck. Two apertures of plain sheet metal were fused into the neck just in front of the cathode. In addition, two metal electrodes were inserted at the point where the neck widened. The purpose of the apertures was to have the cathode ray drawn out into an extremely fine beam. The finer the beam, the smaller the light spot on the fluorescent screen of the glass bulb became. If a constant voltage was applied between the metal electrodes, the beam could be deflected and the light spot raised a little. If the voltage was removed, the spot returned to its old position.

Thomson now proceeded as follows: having shifted the beam with an electric field, he directed it by means of a strong magnetic field back to its original position, which he had previously marked. Measuring instruments inserted into the circuit made precise recordings of the current and voltage required to achieve this. From these figures, taking into account all possible sources of error, Thomson was able to calculate the speed of the particles in the beam. This proved to be rather high, fluctuating, according to the voltage applied, between 12,000 and 24,000 miles per second. To ascertain the precise nature of the particles, information about their mass and the electric charge they carried was essential. From the data Thomson had obtained, he could not deduce this information as such, but only the ratio of the mass to the electric charge. Strangely enough, the result he arrived at was always the same, regardless of whether he operated the tube with a low or a high voltage, whether the amount of residual gas in it was small or large, or whether the electrode was iron, copper, or carbon. The unvarying character of this result suggested that a natural constant of general significance was involved.

Here was one of the strangest cases the physicists had ever encountered. A form of radiation had shown itself to be made up of minutely divided matter—a new substance, so to speak—consisting of particles of unimaginable smallness. These particles originated at the cathode—that is, at the electrode connected to the negative pole of a voltage source. The general view was that this was not something normally described as a "substance," for no new body could be fashioned from it. There seemed more justification for regarding these particles as "atoms of electricity." All electrical phenomena were a sum total of the effects produced by electric charges equal to the charge carried by each particle of the radiation observed. To designate this elementary charge of electricity, the Irish physicist G. Johnstone Stoney introduced the word *electron*. Cathode rays were therefore fast electrons ranging freely through space without being bound to an atom. With the discovery of electrons by Thomson, modern physics began.

Born of Scottish descent in 1856, Joseph John Thomson enrolled, at the early age of fourteen, at Owens College in Manchester, his home town. Advised to apply for a scholarship at Cambridge, he sat for the requisite examination and failed. A year later, in 1876, he passed and entered Trinity College with a minor scholarship. At the age of twenty-seven he was made a Fellow of the Royal Society, and a year later was elected to the Cavendish professorship at Cambridge—the university that had failed him in his first entrance examination. At that time not a few people considered his appointment an unfortunate decision, and one man spoke of a sad state of affairs "when mere boys are made professors."

Joseph John Thomson—or "J.J.," as he was affectionately known—remained a member of Trinity College, in one capacity after another, during the rest of his life. In 1906 he received the Nobel Prize for physics, and was knighted in 1908. He was one of the greatest experimental geniuses of all time; his readiness to use "theory as a policy and not as a creed" give him a unique place among scientists.

"The Moving Finger Writes"

Some years ago the citizens of the German city of Fulda resolved to give their high school a new name connected in some way with science and also, of course, with their own town. A teacher of mathematics and physics suggested that it be named for Karl Ferdinand Braun, but Fulda's educated men knew so little about him that the teacher had to remind Braun's fellow citizens of his achievements. "The discovery that electron beams can be deflected by electric and magnetic fields," the teacher said, "and the possibility of using these beams to make luminescent materials glow prompted Karl Ferdinand Braun to construct a special kind of cathode-ray tube. Braun, a native of this city, was then forty-eight years of age. If today we are able to watch television, in company with millions of people throughout the world, part of the credit is due to Braun. It was his ideas which brought about the birth of the television tube. That tube is nothing more than an improved version of the Braun tube. Furthermore, Braun was in 1909 awarded the Nobel Prize—jointly with Marconi—not, it is true, for inventing his tube, but for other important work in the field of radio technology. It is therefore no more than fitting that we should name our high school after him."

The tube that Braun constructed consisted of a funnel-shaped glass bulb from which air had been evacuated to permit electrons to move inside it without great loss. The cathode was fused in approximately at the middle of the slender neck of the tube. Some distance farther along was a simple screen with a circular aperture, a metal plate with a hole about one fifteenth to two twenty-fifths of an inch wide drilled at its center. If a sufficiently strong voltage was applied between the screen and the cathode, electrons shot out of the cathode in dense clouds. It was already known that electrons can be accelerated in a space where a concentrated amount of electricity is present. They can also be steered by the use of appropriate devices. A vacuum—i.e., a space empty of air—in which there is an electrically charged body is in a state similar to the state prevailing in the neighborhood of a magnet. We picture this space as being threaded with lines of force that act in their turn on electric charges, and therefore on electrons. By adroit arrangement of such electrically active fields, it is possible to shape a whirling mass of free electrons into an extremely fine-drawn beam, and ultimately to steer the beam and move it about. Braun achieved this result with the aforementioned drilled circular screens and a number of magnetic coils.

But the achievement of an electron beam in itself is not the end of the matter because to us it is invisible. What was needed was a special material to transform the energy of the electrons hitting the screen into visible light. Such properties were possessed by all luminescent substances, which had been discovered just at the right time. The chemicals concerned are crystalline substances whose crystal structure is deformed by minute quantities of impurity substances embodied in them. The impact of the electron beam on a mica plate treated with such crystals causes the crystals hit to give off light of varying intensity. If the beam is very coarse—that is, if the electrons in the pencil of rays scatter—the patch of light appearing on the screen is not very bright. If the beam is thin and sharp, only a bright dot appears. Accordingly, through an indirect approach by way of luminescent substances, Braun was able to make the invisible electron beam visible.

If a coil outside the tube carrying an alternating current was brought close to the circular screen, the beam reacted with oscillating movements in accordance with the number of cycles of the alternating current. By this means Braun was able to demonstrate quite a number of oscillatory processes of electrical origin. After undergoing many improvements, this cathode-ray tube was to become an almost unsurpassed instrument for visual observation of any and every kind of oscillatory process.

Later the cathode-ray tube was equipped with a hot cathode, and so-called deflection plates were fused in to replace the drilled screen. But the most important improvement was the oxide cathode. This consists of a little metallic cylinder containing the spiral heater filament, with a layer of oxide applied to the outside of the cylinder. The patch of oxide, which makes it easier for the electrons to emerge from the strongly heated metal, is not much more than one square millimeter in area. In spite of its minute size, it is big enough to supply an adequate stream of electrons for as long as 1,000 hours. During that time the oxide patch loses only a thousandth part of a milligram.

By means of the small metal cylinder, the electrons were drawn out into a fine beam. It was found that the little cylinder, named the *Wehnelt* cylinder after the inventor, not only was a good means of obtaining a very fine electron beam, but also provided an excellent instrument for controlling the electron beam's intensity through application of external voltages. Under the action of a strong electrical impulse, more electrons reach the fluorescent screen than would be the case with a weak impulse. If an electron-poor beam is produced, a weak and rather dim spot of light appears on the screen. If, on the other hand, the number of electrons in the beam is increased, the picture dot brightens.

The cathode-ray tube first won an important place in the research laboratories devoted to industrial and technological problems. For a quarter of a century it was used almost exclusively for visual observation of electrical oscillations, and to record all sorts of curves and characteristics. Later it was applied in testing combustion engines, motor crankshafts, pistons, etc., because it had no destructive effects. But the tube really came into its own when a number of scientists proposed that it be used as "an artificial retina" for receiving television.

It had been known for a long time that bright and dark dots of light, when thrown on a screen in quick succession, produce a useful over-all picture. But how could the dots be thrown fast enough to prevent the eye from noting that it was being deceived?

Through the use of magnetic deflection systems, experimenters now succeeded in guiding the electron beam line by line from left to right and up and down across the fluorescent screen. Originally, a tube of this kind operated with 100 or so lines. The picture was coarse and grainy. Today a television picture twenty-one inches by sixteen inches in size is made up of 625 lines. The electron beam used in such tubes is so finely drawn that the dot it makes, in spite of spread, is no bigger than one two-thousandth of a square inch. A picture twenty-one inches wide and sixteen inches high takes in approximately 670,000 picture dots. That number of picture dots is painted inside one thirtieth of a second, a rate of 20,500,000 picture dots per second. The beam, which paints thirty pictures per second, moves across the surface of the fluorescent screen at a speed of six miles per second. In other words, the beam travels ten times as fast as a rifle bullet. This is the speed required to keep the eye in ignorance of the fact that it is being deceived. The process prevents the eye from seeing that the beam is in motion, that in reality the picture is made up of lines, and that the moving scene is composed, as in films, of single pictures.

With a tube potential of 10,000 volts, the speed at which the electrons are driven along the beam through the tube reaches about 38,000 miles per second. However, before the beam hits the fluorescent layer of the picture screen, it has to pierce an aluminum layer about one ten-thousandth of an inch thick resting on the tips of the coarse grains of the luminescent substance. This aluminum layer, which is deposited on the screen by evaporation, guarantees greater brightness, as it makes possible the use of a higher voltage than an unprotected luminescent layer would permit.

A high degree of vacuum is necessary to ensure that the electron beam can fulfill all the demands made on it. The more complete the vacuum in the tube, the fewer air molecules it contains to obstruct the electrons in their flight. On the other hand, a complete vacuum demands thicker glass walls because it enormously increases the pressure on the tube. Pressure on an entire picture tube of the latest type is approximately 20,000 pounds, the picture surface alone carrying 5,000 pounds—roughly the weight of twenty-eight grown men.

Karl Ferdinand Braun did not live to see the triumph of his tube. The creator of the cathode-ray tube was born in 1850 at Fulda. After taking courses at the universities of Marburg and Berlin, and spending a short period as assistant to Georg Hermann Quincke at the Berlin *Gewerbeakademie* (Industrial Academy), he went to Würzburg to continue his studies. From 1874 to 1876 Braun was principal of a Leipzig high school, and then accepted a professorship at Marburg. In 1895 he became the director of the Institute of Physics at Strasbourg.

Braun, who made a considerable name for himself in the field of wireless telegraphy, obtained support in his work from the firm of Siemens & Halske, which in 1898 founded Prof. Braun's Telegrafie G.m.b.H. (Prof. Braun's Telegraphy Company Limited). At the beginning of World War I, Guglielmo Marconi brought a patent action in an attempt to stop the operations of the transmitting station at Sayville, New York, which had been built and financed by the German Telefunken Company. The only man who could save the situation was Braun. He sailed through the Allied blockade to the United States, fought the action, and successfully asserted the priority of the Telefunken rights. When the United States entered the war in 1917, the Telefunken station was closed down after all, and Braun was interned. The following year he died as a war internee. In 1921 the urn containing Braun's ashes was shipped to Fulda, where it was interred without ceremony.

Twelve years after Braun's death the cathode-ray tube had been modified to a point where it had become practical for television purposes.

Night Vision by Image-Converter Tube

Not infrequently German people walking on a highway on a dark night in the latter part of World War II saw a motorcar without headlights or taillights roar past them at breakneck speed. How could the man at the wheel drive his vehicle at such speed without headlights?

The security veil over the use of infrared headlights and image converters was lifted only toward the end of hostilities. The public learned that for certain night operations armored cars and reconnaissance vehicles had been equipped with "night-driving sets." In essence this equipment was made up of an infrared headlight and an electrical apparatus whose most important constituent was a so-called *image-converter tube*. The headlight did not contain an ordinary electric bulb, but instead used pure carbon or a substance called Beck carbon as a source of radiation. These substances very much weaken the proportion of visible light in favor of infrared rays. The "beam" from a headlight of this kind cannot be made out with night binoculars even at fifty yards' range. An infrared light can be focused like an ordinary headlight, and its beam behaves in exactly the same way as visible light. The moment it comes up against a body of any sort, it is partially reflected by that body. If these reflected infrared rays are guided onto an infrared-sensitive screen, electrons are dislodged by the impact of the invisible rays. These electrons can be focused by an electrostatic focusing lens in such a way that a strong electron beam is produced. The beam is now directed onto a fluorescent screen, a mica plate that shows dots of light the moment it is struck by fast electrons.

By this method infrared light can be made visible. However, as we have already said, infrared light is not reflected equally by all objects. We know that chlorophyll reflects it more strongly than a water surface does, and such differences naturally become apparent on the fluorescent screen of the image-converter tube. The result is an *infrared picture* which, though it does not conform to the conventional notion of a picture, can nevertheless be used for orientation purposes.

The first models of the *night-driving set* had a visibility range of about 200 yards. Tanks equipped with much more powerful versions of these devices could discern targets at a range of something over 3,000 yards. While the war was still in progress, the instruments were so much improved that even in pitch darkness and in dense fog the picture of an irradiated object could be seen at still greater distances.

At the end of the war American troops seized vehicles equipped with night-driving gear. These devices have since been considerably developed, and all armies are conversant with them. It is now known that with the aid of lead-sulfide cells the effective range of the night-driving gear has been raised to fifteen miles. This is far superior to the night vision even of many members of the cat family.

During the war German physicists also developed a variant of the night-driving set—a special telescopic sight that could be mounted on a rifle. It enabled a sharpshooter to align his sights on a man at several hundred yards' range in total darkness. The telescopic sight contained a special image-converter tube for infrared rays operating at a voltage of no less than 15,000 volts. The precision with which this sight had been constructed is shown by the fact that allowance had even been made for electron deviation inside the image-converter tube due to the magnetic field, weak in itself, of the earth. It should be pointed out that free electrons can also be influenced by magnetic fields, which deflect them from their original path. Hence it was necessary to set up a field that as far as possible neutralized the magnetic field of the earth.

If the construction of the small image-converter tube, not much larger in size than two matchboxes placed side by side, was a technological masterpiece, the little power-generating unit was even more so.

The entire unit was approximately six inches in diameter. It consisted of a flashlight battery, a transformer, and a motor the size of a walnut which converted the 4.5-volt direct voltage to alternating voltage. This motor worked at 10,000 revolutions per minute, and the tiny bearings were at first deformed and rendered unserviceable by this high rpm rate. The large amount of ozone produced spoiled any normal commercial lubricating oil. Not until an ozone-proof lubricant was used could the little motor perform its function. It was designed for a running time of 3,000 hours. The miniature transformer stepped up the potential from 4.5 volts to 15,000 volts, and this was then again rectified. The mystery apparatus was carried in a linen bag on the rifleman's back. The rifle was equipped with two triggers. The first was pressed to bring the power supply into operation, at the same time making the image-converter tube ready for action. The rifleman could now look about for an enemy target. Having detected him and aligned his sights, he pulled the second trigger that fired the shot.

The development of efficient infrared image-converter tubes was the result of a great deal of effort. But how was their individual efficiency to be tested on the basis of invariable infrared light? One day a physicist remembered that there is a star situated close to the extreme tip of the Great Bear's tail which emits infrared light only (this is why that star was not discovered for so long). Now, if a tube were sound, the star would be found without trouble; otherwise, it would be sought in vain.

In the course of the observations, it was also discovered that the disk of the planet Mars appears larger through an infrared telescope than when looked at through a conventional telescope. This discovery was interpreted to mean that Mars possesses an atmosphere that reflects infrared rays.

Today image-converter sets are put into operation wherever ordinary light cannot be used: in fog, in mist, and at night. They are employed in night hunts for criminals, in tracking down smugglers, and, as in the last war, for reconnaissance in enemy territory.

The Electron Microscope

The best light microscope cannot magnify an object more than 3,000 times—not because of man's inability to improve the technical performance of microscopes, but because particles smaller in size than half the wave length of violet light cannot be "resolved." In other words, the light ray is too "coarse."

A way out of this dilemma was offered by ultraviolet rays, which are, of course, shorter than the light rays in the visible optical range. But where these rays are employed, direct use of the eyes has to be abandoned, and the picture can be made available for visual observation only through the medium of a photographic plate. By this means, objects can be magnified 5,000 times. To achieve even more far-reaching resolution, we have to relinquish normal glass lenses and resort to even shorter waves. But, scientists asked themselves, where were such rays to be obtained? Were they to have recourse to X rays, which adjoin the ultra-violet rays in the electromagnetic spectrum? This was impossible, because up to now no means has been found of handling X rays *optically* in the manner of light rays. What, then, was to be done to produce a microscope with which a greater degree of resolution could be achieved?

In 1924 the Frenchman Prince Louis de Broglie demonstrated that cathode rays have a definite wave length, depending on their speed. In certain circumstances the wave length may be a thousand times shorter than that of visible light. But if cathode rays manifest themselves in the form of waves, they must to a certain degree behave optically—that is, optically in an electronic sense. It must be possible to collect, refract, and spread them. This line of thought was put forward two years later by Hans Busch of Darmstadt, Germany, who spoke of a new kind of optics, "electron optics." It had been known since 1898 that current-carrying coils show the properties of lenses in relation to electron beams. At that time the German physicist H. Weichert had found out that when an electric current passes through toroidal coils they affect electron beams in a manner similar to the way lenses affect light rays. The new feature of Busch's work was the mathematical treatment of the problem; with the laws and formulas that he worked out, he practically laid the foundation of electron optics and, beyond this, of a series of inventions of which the *electron microscope* is the finest and most significant.

The name *electron microscope* might lead one to suppose that this instrument can be used for visual observation of electrons. But in the electron microscope, electrons merely take over the role played by light rays in the light micro-scope. However, owing to their considerably shorter wave length, electrons do a much better job. For example, they make possible a degree of picture resolution roughly a hun-dred times greater than is achieved by light rays. That means that we are not restricted, as in the case of the light micro-scope, to seeing particles of sizes ranging down to 0.0002 millimeters at best, but that they may be as small as 0.000006 millimeters. To put it another way: the degree of magnification achieved with electron beams is not 3,000 times, but 300,000 times. In other words, we see particles of inconceivable smallness 300,000 times as long and 300,-000 times as broad as they really are, and the resultant area accordingly offers 30 billion times as many details as we could otherwise discern.

Basically, the electron microscope consists of a high-vacuum envelope in which fast electrons are focused and directed by special lens systems. The interesting thing is that these "lenses" are made not of glass, as in the light miscroscope, but of metal plates or wire coils, according to the nature of the model used. We saw earlier that electron beams can be influenced by electric or magnetic fields. Using these fields, we can deflect the beams, focus them, or spread them, in other words, treat them in the same way as we treat light rays with various types of glass lens. In es-sence, there is nothing simpler than one of these electron lenses. An electrostatic system, for instance, merely con-sists of three plates, each of them perforated and all three close together. If we apply a high negative potential to the hole in the middle disk and pass a broad electron beam through the foremost disk, the electrostatic field inside the perforation compresses the beam. The broad, thick beam becomes a fine one. We can, of course, restore the wide beam or concentrate it in a fine point, like light rays in a magnifying glass. Practically speaking, we can maneuver the beam in the same way as light in a microscope, except that the means used are different. In the case of magnetic electron lenses the agent is a magnetic field of the kind found between the pole pieces of a powerful electromagnet.

Let us now picture a very thoroughly evacuated tube. In it there is an arrangement acting as a source of electrons similar to that in a radio tube: a strongly heated piece of wire which emits clouds of electrons. To marshal these for the purpose of creating an image, they are passed through a series of electron lenses on their way to the anode. Each and every one of these lenses has a special function to perform. The object is to create an electron trajectory corresponding in terms of light optics to the ray of a normal microscope. If, now, at a particular point in the path of the rays we introduce an object, which we have to encapsule in the metal tube, the electrons are scattered. This scattering does not depend, as in the normal microscope, on the color and the refraction index, but on the density of the object. Other lenses collect the electron beam again, focus it, and concentrate it in a point. Next the beam is directed onto a large folding fluorescent screen that can be removed from the path of the beam for photographic purposes, and that glows with varying intensity according to the strength of the incoming stream of electrons. A picture of the object, hugely magnified, is now thrown on the screen. Of course, the magnified image is in effect only a shadow of the object of which an enlarged version is required. In more recent models the picture can be observed with both eyes from the front, and from both sides through large lead glass windows. Lead glass is necessary because it protects the eyes against any X rays emitted in the process.

In Germany experiments in electron optics were carried out by the Technische Hochschule in Berlin and the AEG[1] Research Institute. In 1931 the Technische Hochschule

[1] Allgemeine Elektrizitätsgesellschaft, a leading German electrical corporation. (Translator's note)

completed the first experimental model; this electron microscope, built by M. Knoll and Ernst Ruska, operated with electromagnetic lenses. However, its resolving power was much inferior to that of an ordinary light microscope. In 1933-4 Ruska constructed the first absorption microscope with high magnification—which in resolving power and magnifying power far exceeded even the best light microscope. In the meantime H. Mahl of the AEG Research Institute had succeeded in constructing the first electrostatic electron supermicroscope, in which electrostatic lenses were used instead of magnetic lenses. Only in the late thirties did industry take a serious interest in these devices.

Advancing into Unknown Worlds

There is scarcely a single field of scientific research that has not been enriched by the invention of the electron microscope.

Let us consider one great biological and medical riddle alone: the virus. Up to now, we have been able to make a fairly close study of about one third of all the known virus types. Without the electron microscope, that would never have been possible, for most viruses are too small to be seen with even the best light microscope.

The first virus that was brought into visual range by the electron microscope was the celebrated *tobacco-mosaic virus*. Mosaic disease is an ailment, much feared by farmers, of potatoes, tomatoes, tobacco, and other plants of the nightshade family. It was called by that name because the leaves of plants affected by the virus show bright, mosaic-like blotches in places where the chlorophyll, so important to the plants, has been destroyed. The virus is carried by plant lice.

Studies of this plant disease have been going on since 1892, but for a long time no one was able to find the cause.

It was not revealed by the light microscope, and researchers therefore quite rightly conjectured that the organism concerned must be far beyond the limit of resolution of light rays. The scientists were, however, not in the least discouraged by this conclusion: on the contrary, it made the disease all the more interesting. Wendell Meredith Stanley, an American biochemist, was the man who finally succeeded in isolating the virus after he had crushed and refrigerated five tons of tobacco leaves afflicted with mosaic disease. Under the electron microscope it proved to be a rod-shaped object that was chemically soluble and could be recrystallized. Since then the virus has set the investigators many puzzles, puzzles that are by no means all solved even now.

Among the largest viruses are those which cause smallpox. About 150 millionths of a millimeter in size, they were first detected by the German Enrique Paschen, using the electron microscope. The smallest viruses are globules about 20 millionths of a millimeter in diameter. They have a molecular weight (by which we mean the sum of the atomic weights of their constituent atoms) of about 3 to 8 million. If, for instance, we calculate the molecular weight of common salt (sodium = 23 plus chlorine = 35.46), we obtain a figure of 58.46. We realize from this that even the smallest virus types are giant molecules, such as are encountered almost exclusively in organic chemistry.

The viruses next in size to the smallest have the form of fibers. They are 15 millionths of a millimeter in diameter and 300 millionths of a millimeter in length. Viruses like these have molecular weights of 40 million or more. Compared with an oxygen molecule (molecular weight 2 × 16), they are veritable giants. If we imagine them as ball-shaped objects, the radius of each encompasses the length of 50 to 100 atoms placed end to end. Yet such virus globules are so minute that a quadrillion of them could be accommodated in an area of one cubic millimeter. One of the most important discoveries about viruses made by means of the electron microscope is the fact that a virus consists of a nucleus and a shell. The electron microscope distinguishes clearly between denser substances inside the virus and less dense matter in the outer zone.

Another interesting discovery was the *bacteriophages,* the bacteria-eaters. Their destructive activity has been photographed, and it is evident from the pictures that the phages attach themselves to the bodies of bacteria like ticks. They bore into the cell wall and break up the nucleus. The electronic picture shows bacteria shells split open, with phages sticking out of them. In other photographs we see the bodies of bacteria stuffed with phages like tightly packed sausages. Most interesting of all are the phages themselves. In shape they resemble tadpoles, with a clearly recognizable "head" and "tail." This tail is not used for purposes of propulsion; it serves rather as an instrument for penetrating the cell, a process in which, as can be seen, the firmer cell sheath is punctured. The remarkable feature is that after the tail has penetrated into the body of the bacterium, the rest of the phage's body is cast off, without affecting the cell-destroying function.

With the electron microscope it was also possible to make a closer study of bacteria and bacilli that had long been known. The fact that the intricacies of their structure could now be seen supplied medical science with important pointers to effective methods of combating them. Under magnification of "only" 10,000 times, it is clearly apparent that staphylococci, the dreaded pus-forming microbes, globular bacteria growing in clusters like grapes, move with the aid of propeller-like flagella. If the familiar gas-gangrene bacilli are magnified 13,000 times, we see alongside them queer-looking, rectangular, capsule-like objects that had previously eluded observation. Another discovery has brought to light details, unknown before, of the microbes that cause epidemic cerebrospinal meningitis. Under the light microscope, the bacillus of chicken tuberculosis appears at best as a small fiber; when magnified 26,000 times by the electron microscope, it looks like a fully grown worm.

In other areas of research, too, the electron microscope brought new knowledge. Asbestos, magnified 30,000 times, was shown to consist of thin fibers, some of them only one three-hundred-thousandth of a millimeter wide, and even of these many were split.

Since research with the electron microscope was begun, a great many results previously arrived at have been revised. It has been possible to prove that the earlier conception of the structure of the red pigment in blood was wrong. Similarly, many uncertainties in the field of dust and soot technology have been removed.

Investigation by electron microscope has taught manufacturers how coloring materials adhere to silk, cotton, and wool. Smoke, argillaceous earth, and insecticides have yielded up their secrets. This microscope has shown the safety engineer that, contrary to previous assumptions, blasting dust contains many minute particles of drilling dust which could cause dangerous explosions.

A particularly broad field has been opened up for the metallurgist. Examined under the light microscope, ground metal sections or surfaces used to look relatively smooth. Under the electron microscope, however, even highly polished surfaces present the appearance of newly plowed land full of furrows and grooves, while ball-bearing channels resemble dirty, rutted roads churned up by heavy tractor traffic or armored vehicles.

Photographs of macromolecules were shown for the first time at the International Congress of Electron Microscopy that took place in Paris in September 1950. As we have already mentioned, macromolecules are giant molecules found extensively in organic matter; they are synthetically prepared in the plastics industry. Magnified 100,000 times under the electron microscope, these monsters among the molecules were just barely recognizable as fuzzy, amorphous specks. In Paris the German scientist Erwin W. Müller showed the arrangement of the atoms in the molecules not in photographs, as the speakers before him had done, but by direct projection onto a screen. In the course of this demonstration the molecules could be observed "live," as it were, enlarged as never before and with all their movement under the influence of heat visible on the screen. The most astonishing thing of all was the staggering simplicity of Müller's apparatus—a form of electron microscope without any actual electron lenses.

The knowledge that electrons emerge with particular ease from sharp points is almost as old as the science of electrostatics. But no one could have foreseen that this effect would one day be used for visual demonstration of the arrangement of atoms in molecules—in fact, of the atoms themselves.

In 1936 when Erwin W. Müller was a young candidate for a doctor's degree, he had set out from the idea that electrons emerging from very sharp metal points behave in a manner similar to extremely fine pollen that is blown onto a pane of glass through a tightly meshed grating. The mesh pattern is reproduced on the glass plate, the pollen appearing only where the lattice holes are. By analogy, electrons flying off a sharp point could outline molecules and atoms lying in their path if an appropriately curved fluorescent screen were placed some distance from the point so that the impact of electrons hitting it could make it glow.

Naturally, the point would have to be an extremely fine one connected to the negative pole of a voltage source. The position of the anode inside the tube would be immaterial. It had been known for a long time that electrons fly perpendicularly off the surface of the point (the cathode), regardless of the position of the anode. Special electronic optical equipment, such as is necessary in the case of electron microscopes, would be entirely superfluous here. Such was the reasoning of the young doctor-to-be.

His apparatus, which was ready for operation as early as 1937 and was named the *field emission electron microscope*, consists essentially of an evacuated ball-shaped glass container housing a fluorescent screen, a ring-shaped anode, and, most important of all, a piece of tungsten wire with an extremely fine point as a cathode. If a potential of several thousand volts is applied between the ring anode and the cathode, a field intensity of some 40 to 100 million volts per centimeter is produced, owing to the small surface of the cathode point: this has a radius of a few ten-thousandths of a millimeter or less. The high field intensity is sufficient to wrench electrons out of the cathode point in adequately large numbers, even in the cold state. Most of the electrons that burst out from among the lattice holes of the molecules shoot perpendicularly off the cathode surface and fly almost straight at the fluorescent screen. If the screen is roughly ten centimeters away and the radius of the cathode point is one ten-thousandth of a millimeter, the result is that the cathode point is magnified a million times. Bright and dark zones or areas appear on the fluorescent screen arranged in a symmetrical pattern, and reveal details of the molecules and the position of their constituent atoms.

In contrast to the electron microscope, the field emission electron microscope developed by Erwin W. Müller can display only objects and activity on the metal surface of the cathode point.

Accelerating Electrons

An electric-potential field exists in the space surrounding unneutralized electric charges. Electrons influenced by the field have a tendency to move in such a manner as to neutralize the charges creating the field. As soon as all the charges have been neutralized, the flow of electric current stops.

In other words, a flow of electrons takes place only in the presence of unneutralized charges. Any electron, whether a conduction electron in a metal or a free electron in space, will behave in the same manner. It will always steer a course toward a point where there is a shortage of electrons. If there is a potential difference of one volt between two metal plates separated by air, the free electron will always move from the negative to the positive charge. In doing so, the electron develops a definite speed: in our example, about 2×10^6 feet or 370 miles per second. If the plates are an inch apart, this distance will therefore be covered by an electron in 4.2×10^{-8} (42 billionths) of a second. The energy attained by electrons under the influence of a potential of one volt is called an *electron volt*. This quantity of energy corresponds to the minute figure of 1.602 trillionths of an erg or roughly 380 quintillionths of a calorie.

Cathode rays are, as we know, powerfully accelerated beams of electrons. As long as these rays move at a speed of no more than 10,000 to 30,000 miles per second, their increase in weight is not considerable. Since 1930, however, efforts have been in progress to increase the mass of electrons by the use of the highest possible potentials. We are now actually in a position to produce cathode rays bearing electrons almost at the speed of light. In fact, cathode rays are already being produced with speed no more than one per cent short of the speed of light. At these velocities, the mass of accelerated electrons is ten times their mass at rest. At present we have a variety of procedures for achieving high acceleration of electrons. For this purpose we use *electron accelerators*.

In principle, the electron accelerator or *betatron* is a transformer. In the case of a common type of transformer an alternating voltage that is applied to the primary winding can be stepped up or down and appears at the terminals of the secondary winding. In the electron accelerator the secondary winding consists of only one turn. In practice, this is made in the form of a ring-shaped tube in which electrons can circulate freely. The magnetic field of the transformer is so arranged that the electrons are always obliged to remain in the middle of the tube, no matter how heavy they may become. Today electron accelerators of huge dimensions are being built. Even in the smaller types the path along which the electrons travel is eight feet in diameter. The electrons are shot in with an energy of 80,000 volts, and gain about 3,000 volts each time they make a circuit inside the porcelain tube. Each circuit is about twenty-six feet long. The maximum energy the electrons can attain in such an apparatus is 320 million electron volts. To attain this high velocity, the electrons have to make 100,000 circuits of the tube. In doing so, they travel 600 miles, roughly the distance from New York to Cincinnati. From the time the electrons are enclosed until they reach their maximum velocity, only one hundredth of a second elapses. Cathode rays carrying particles accelerated to about 100 million electron volts can be identified in a free space at a distance of fifty yards. If such a cathode ray is directed at a very hard metal—such as tungsten, for example—the latter will very soon show blister-like bulges that burst open in the manner of boils and leave crater-shaped cavities behind. Calc-spar crystals placed in the path of the rays flare up with a dazzling light equal to several hundred candle power. Its brilliance does not die down even after the electron accelerator has been switched off for several hours, yet the crystals remain completely cold. Air has been made to glow in the same way, while insulating materials exposed to cathode rays for some time change color completely and become conductors.

Electron accelerators have been shown to achieve good results in healing malignant tumors. Animal tissues have a low absorption factor for fast electrons. Electron beams accelerated to a velocity of "only" 2.5 million electron volts penetrate tissue to a depth of a quarter of an inch, whereas electron beams of 30 million electron volts can be used to reach practically any part of the human body.

Cathode rays produced in electron accelerators possess a radiation intensity comparable to that of 220 pounds of radium. If we bear in mind the fact that the total stock of natural radium on earth amounts to no more than three pounds at most, we get a rough idea of the vast energies shut up in these highly accelerated electrons.

Electron Beams from the Sun

"Once more Almighty God hath set a token of His righteous wrath before our eyes, which many hundred persons not only saw, but whereof they gave manifold and diverse meanings. Thus at the onset it showed itself as a mighty rainbow by night, with shining spears and here and there shooting flames of fire, as were the sound of horsemen and cuirassiers and ofttimes shots and detonations to be heard. In sum, it looked in earnest and seemed for all the world a most fiery battle. Yet what this prodigious token may portend is beyond man's power certainly to read. Time alone will best construe it. Let God the Saviour grant all may yet be well. Amen."

So ran a contemporary account of a strange apparition in the heavens which was observed on January 25, 1630— during the Thirty Years' War—in the neighborhood of Tübingen in Germany. On January 25, 1938—308 years later to the day—the northern lights, a phenomenon rarely seen in central Europe, were observed again; and again superstitious folk spoke of imminent war, famine, and pestilence.

What are these northern lights and how do they occur? They appear in a variety of forms and colors, mostly in high latitudes. Often they are seen as great arches in the sky, reddish, greenish, and bluish in hue. They also present themselves in the form of garlands that now hang still, now quiver and oscillate violently. The loveliest, but also the rarest, of these polar phenomena is the "dome of light," which reaches like a vaulted chamber high into the heavens, with brilliant shafts of light streaking out on either side. Sometimes, too, the northern lights are seen in the shape of broad pencils of rays narrowing upward to a point in the direction of the magnetic axis of inclination. This manifestation points most clearly to the part played by the earth's magnetic forces in creating the aurora borealis.

On our sun, dynamic processes of vast proportions are constantly in progress. Huge masses of boiling vapor, mostly from calcium and hydrogen layers under the photosphere (the luminous envelope of the sun), pour out of craters so big that it would take thousands of globes the size of the earth to fill them. The violence of the erupting gases produces whirlwinds of unimaginable turbulence. The masses of gas that belch forth often reach a height of several hundred thousand miles within a short space of time. The greatest of these *prominences* (the name given to the blasts of hot gas) so far observed was photographed from the Mount Wilson Observatory on July 27, 1937. The tongue of gas in question attained a height of approximately 600,000 miles in just two hours.

The vapors that burst forth from the mighty abysses and craters on the surface of the sun are almost always followed by giant clouds of expelled electrons. They reach the earth like the beam of some immense searchlight. The period involved, resulting from the rotation of the sun and the revolution of the earth around it, is about twenty-seven days. In that time the earth moves into the beam of this electron searchlight again and again, and on some days its spread is so great that the earth remains for some time under its influence. Then the magnetic needles start to quiver and dance; the automatic Morse telegraphs, as if touched by some magician's hand, begin chattering out a chaotic jumble of incomprehensible code. In the large power plants in northern latitudes, ground currents are set up which produce such a strong flow in the normally current-free neutral conductors of the high-voltage cables that automatic fuses are brought into play, while long-range radio communication is rendered impossible for hours at a stretch. The operators switch off their instruments with an air of resignation and talk about a "magnetic storm."

The electrons that are shot off the sun in huge clouds travel at a speed of approximately 1,100 miles per second. They cover the distance between the sun and the earth in about two days. When these electrons enter the outer belts of gas around the globe, they are diverted toward the poles by the earth's magnetic field. The collision between the electrons and molecules of nitrogen and oxygen touches off a glow across hundreds of thousands of square miles of the atmosphere, the unearthly light particularly associated with the aurora borealis. This feat of nature's may very well be compared with the process in a neon tube, where electrons in collision with neon atoms likewise produce luminous effects.

While the predominantly green color of the northern lights was known to be due to nitrogen atoms, an especially characteristic green line occurring in the spectrum of the northern lights, called the *northern-lights line*, suggested the presence of another gas, as yet unknown, at the uppermost levels of the atmosphere. To clear up this point, ordinary nitrogen was liquefied and converted into solid crystalline form. Under spectroscopic examination the mysterious northern-lights line showed up alongside the other lines. This proved that the green color of the northern lights can only be caused by nitrogen atoms. The blue and violet colors are produced by oxygen atoms. A grayish-blue tone shading off gently into violet arises when the blue of the northern lights is topped by the red-seeming light of the midnight sun.

Effects like those of the northern lights have also been demonstrated in the laboratory by means of a model iron globe suspended in an evacuated container. The iron globe, representing the earth, was magnetized. When an electron beam was sent into the glass vessel from one side, it was deflected toward the polar caps. The ultimate result was that the very rarefied air at the poles became luminous in familiar belts of whitish-blue in the manner of the northern lights. Whether the electron beam was steered toward the "equator" or directly at the polar caps of the model globe, it hit the surface of the earth only in the vicinity of the magnetic pole. This experiment was filmed a number of times. The photographs show clearly that there is an electron-free region lying like a ring around the equator. The northern lights are therefore "children of the sun" caused by masses of electrons originating on the surface of the sun which, before they ever reach the earth's surface, are grasped by a giant fist and turned toward the poles. There they set thin gases aglow, sometimes on such a scale that the display of lights can be seen even in more southern latitudes.

CHAPTER 6

Herr Rautgen's Discovery

ON JANUARY 9, 1896, a newspaper at Würzburg, Germany, ran a short notice to the effect that a Herr Rautgen of Vienna "has discovered a light which, when used in photography, penetrates wood, meat, and the majority of other materials. . . ." Around that date other newspapers also reported "on a photographic discovery," always with the added comment that this "is not a matter of a joke or humbug," but a serious discovery on the part of a reputable professor in Vienna.

The papers showered their readers with fanciful reports. They spoke of a "light" that passed through walls, of rays that had made possible long-range vision, of spectacles from which nothing could remain concealed. The *Electrical World*, a specialist journal, called the discovery a menace. Private life had ceased to exist, it asserted, when photographs could be taken through thick walls. And the highly respectable *Pall Mall Gazette* of London declared that wasting words on anything so disgraceful would be superfluous. All civilized nations should unite, it said, to burn works on these rays.

What had actually occurred?

Since October 1895, Wilhelm Conrad Röntgen, Director of the Institute of Physics at Würzburg, had been engaged in studying the properties of discharge phenomena with various types of Geissler discharge tubes. In the course of one of his experiments—it was on November 8 "at a late hour of the evening when all employees had left the laboratory" —he noticed that the glass walls of one of the discharge tubes he had in operation was emitting a kind of radiation. He had previously wrapped this tube in black paper with the object of being better able to test the transparency of different kinds of paper. The radiation had caught his attention by sheer accident. Near the tube lay a box of luminescent substance in powder form which suddenly and without apparent reason began to give off light in the darkness. Röntgen now held the nearest thing to hand—a small board—in the presumed path of the rays. The powder went on glowing, if somewhat more feebly. His thoughts turned to his luminescent screen, by then a normal piece of equipment in every physics laboratory. He moved it in front of the tube, and it immediately began to fluoresce. When he switched off the tube, the glow vanished from the screen. The rays causing the glow were invisible, but they undoubtedly came from the tube itself. Particularly astonishing was the fact that even when he pushed a thick book of about a thousand pages between the tube and the screen, the fluorescence on the screen did not vanish. He concluded that the radiation must have an enormous power of penetration. From his knowledge, Röntgen could not recall any kind of ray exhibiting such properties.

The ensuing days were to bring an additional surprise. While the tube was in operation, Röntgen had grasped the bulbous end simply to turn it in another direction, and as his hand was interposed between the bulb and the luminescent screen, he saw—for a fraction of a second, the length of time his hand was not moving—the hand clearly delineated as a shadowy bone outline on the screen. He repeated the ex-

Changing the structure of organic materials by nuclear radiation.
[Sovfoto]

The Engineering Test Reactor: pressure vessel and core.
[*courtesy:* NATIONAL REACTOR TESTING STATION, IDAHO]

Injection equipment connected to the cosmotron at Brookhaven National Laboratory (Upton, Long Island, New York). [*courtesy:* ASSOCIATED UNIVERSITIES, INC.]

A mobile personnel shield, developed by Argonne National Laboratory (Lemont, Illinois), which permits the remote handling of radioactive material. [*courtesy:* ARGONNE NATIONAL LABORATORY]

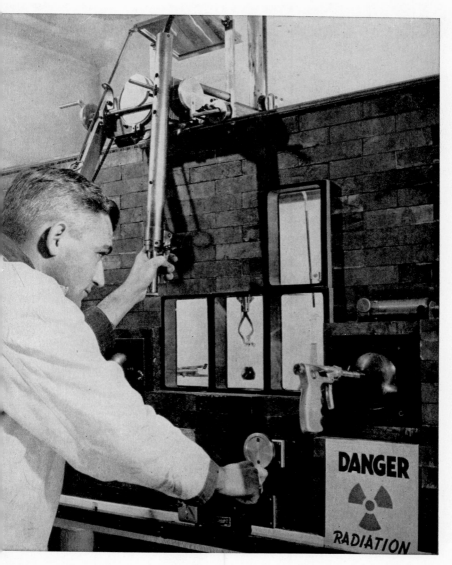

A chemist at Brookhaven National Laboratory uses a re-
mote-control manipulator to handle radioactive liquid behind a protective wall of lead bricks and special lead glass.
[*courtesy:* Brookhaven National Laboratory]

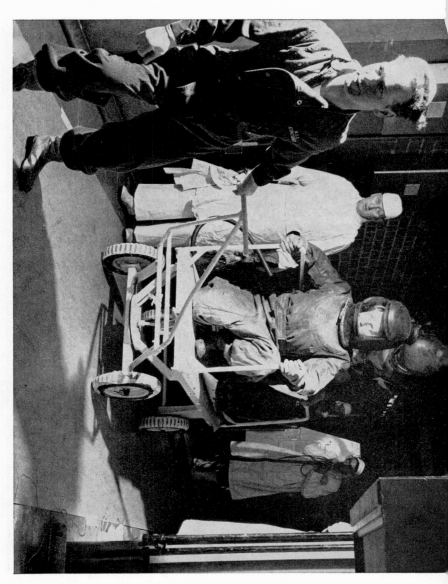

Maintenance workers in an atomic plant are transferred by trolley from one section of the building to another. This is done so that radioactive dust, which may have contaminated their protective clothing, will not be spread to other parts of the building. [BRITISH OFFICIAL PHOTOGRAPH. CROWN COPYRIGHT RESERVED]

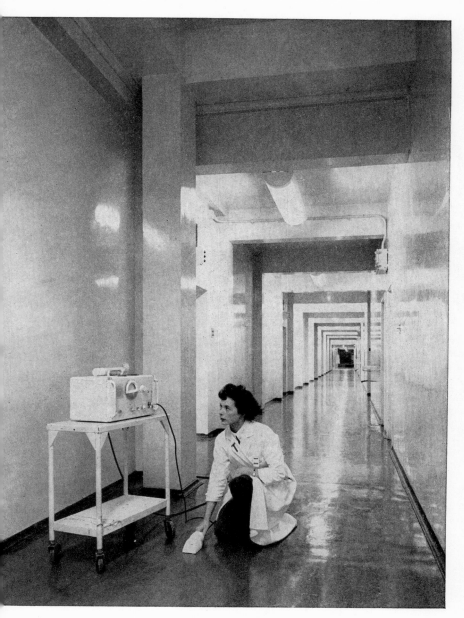

At the Windscale plutonium factory (Cumberland, England) an employee checks a corridor floor for radioactivity. The machine on the trolley ticks loudly if there is the slightest trace of activity; the tag pinned to the girl's coat will record any cumulative radiation she has been exposed to during her duties. [*courtesy:* UNITED KINGDOM INFORMATION SERVICES]

The Wilson Cloud Chamber at Brookhaven National Laboratory (Upton, Long Island, New York) is used for cosmic-ray studies. [*courtesy:* BROOKHAVEN NATIONAL LABORATORY]

periment, with the same result. Röntgen realized that these strange rays coming from his experimental tube made it possible to see into the interior of a body. A few days later Röntgen remarked to the anatomist Rudolf Albert von Kölliker: "I have discovered something extremely interesting, but I don't know whether my observations are correct." For the time being, Röntgen gave away no further details of his discovery. He worked in seclusion in his laboratory, and even made arrangements to sleep there. On December 22 he took the first X-ray photograph: a picture of his wife's hand, the bones of which were clearly reproduced. "Now hell can be let loose," Röntgen is then supposed to have said.

On December 28, 1895, he submitted to the President of the Physikalisch-Medizinische Gesellschaft (Physical and Medical Society) his first report on the subject under the title: "Concerning a New Kind of Radiation." "If the discharges of a Rühmkorff apparatus are passed through a Hittorf tube in a completely darkened room," the report said, "the tube being covered with a fairly close-fitting sheath of thin cardboard, and if a paper screen coated with barium cyanoplatinite is then placed close to the apparatus, the screen is observed to glow brightly at every discharge, regardless of whether the coated side or the other side of the screen is turned toward the discharge apparatus. The fluorescence is visible six feet from the apparatus. It is an easy matter to convince oneself that the cause of the fluorescence comes from the discharge apparatus and from no other point in the circuit."

The President had Röntgen's report printed at once. According to custom, Röntgen dispatched offprints to a number of friends, and one went to a man named Karl Flexl in Vienna. Enclosed with the letter to Flexl was a photograph showing the bone structure of the hand of Röntgen's wife. Flexl showed the picture to a friend of his, the son of the editor-in-chief of a Viennese daily. A short report on the discovery was put together at the newspaper office the same day, so hastily that the name Röntgen was misspelled and appeared as "Rautgen." London picked up the sensational story and cabled it around the world; by January 8 the report was rolling off the American rotary presses. Finally, on the 9th, the *Würzburger Zeitung* carried the news. But as yet nobody in Würzburg suspected that "Herr Rautgen of Vienna" was none other than their own Professor Röntgen.

In laboratories across the world where an induction apparatus and discharge tubes were available, scientists now began to take X-ray photographs. Röntgen received letters by the bagful and was bombarded with inquiries. But he remained silent. The Kaiser commanded him to give an account of his discovery in Berlin, and bestowed the Order of the Crown, Second Class, upon him.

Then came the day on which Röntgen reported in a lecture to the Physikalisch-Medizinische Gesellschaft. He described his discovery in simple terms, praised the work of his predecessors, and passed around several X-ray photographs. At the conclusion of his statement he asked Kölliker, a member of the audience, to allow his hand to be photographed under the rays, and the celebrated anatomist assented. The photograph was immediately developed and shown. Kölliker thereupon asked permission to address the meeting. Speaking with profound emotion, he said: "In all the forty-eight years during which I have belonged to this society, I have never yet attended a session in which matters of such great moment were expounded as those we have heard today. . . . I propose that in future these unknown rays be called 'Röntgen rays,' and I request that the name be recorded in the minutes of this meeting."

Wilhelm Conrad Röntgen was born at Lennep in the Rhineland on March 27, 1845, the son of a merchant and cloth manufacturer who had married a cousin from Amsterdam. Wilhelm spent his youth in Holland; he attended the *Gymnasium* at Utrecht. A students' prank in which he himself had scarcely any part brought his school days to an abrupt end before graduation; Röntgen was expelled because he had refused to reveal the name of the fellow student who had drawn a cartoon of a teacher on the blackboard. Finally allowed, by way of exception, to sit for the final examination, he failed to pass. As he could not enroll at any German university without a proper graduation certificate, he registered at the *Polytechnikum* in Zurich, Switzerland, an institution of university rank. In 1868 Röntgen obtained a doctorate with a dissertation on gases.

In the same year he became the assistant of August Kundt, a German physicist who had been appointed professor at the *Polytechnikum*. When Kundt two years later was offered a chair at Würzburg, he persuaded Röntgen to go with him. Röntgen later followed Kundt to Strasbourg as well. In 1879 he went to the University of Giessen, and eleven years afterward succeeded the renowned Friedrich Kohlrausch in the chair of physics at Würzburg—from where Röntgen's fame was to be carried to every corner of the globe.

In spite of the commotion caused by his discovery Röntgen remained an extremely modest man. Nor did he for a moment think of material advantages. When representatives of the AEG concern approached him with a proposal to cooperate in exploiting his discovery commercially, he is said to have flared up at the mere word "patents." He took the view that his scientific discoveries were common property and must not be preserved by patent for the benefit of private enterprise or for his own benefit.

In 1899 Röntgen was made professor of physics at the University of Munich. The first Nobel Prize for physics (1901) went to him. He refused to use the title of nobility conferred upon him by the Bavarian royal house and omitted to have the title recorded in the register of noble families. The sum of money he had received with the Nobel Prize was made over to the University of Würzburg. Rontgen, who had still been teaching experimental physics as a septuagenarian, died on February 10, 1923, at his home in Weilheim, Bavaria.

X Rays Akin to Light

Until 1912 no one had a clear idea of the nature of X rays. It was conjectured that they were a form of wave radiation like light. But there was no means of determining their wave length. The wave length of light is usually ascertained by means of an instrument called a simple-line, or diffraction, grating. It consists of metal plates on which fine lines are engraved and which are placed face to face a short distance apart. If light is allowed to enter them at a certain angle, the colors of the spectrum appear, and on the basis of these colors the wave length can be determined. However, this method is suitable only for light of a relatively long wave length. It does not work with X rays because simple-line gratings prove too coarse for the purpose. The shorter the wave length, the closer together the lines on the grating must be; but to make gratings of such delicate design is technically impossible. How, then, could the wave length of X rays be ascertained?

In the search for a suitable instrument, it occurred to the German physicist Max von Laue that the inner structure of crystals might supply such a test grating. However, the trellised structure of crystals was at that time purely a matter of theory. Laue launched appropriate experiments in which crystals were irradiated with X rays. The very first photographs revealed the wonderfully orderly pattern of molecules and atoms inside the crystals, and also proved that the structure of crystals was trellised in form. Now a means of measuring the wave length of X rays had been found. The lattice structure of crystals was a yardstick such as the physicists could not wish to better.

Over and above this, it was now possible to measure the distances between the atoms in the crystals. While the wave lengths of X rays were being determined, it became evident that X rays, like sunlight, do not form a uniform type of radiation, but rather that here, too, there is a spectrum, for the investigation of which special spectroscopes had to be constructed. Measurements showed that the mean wave length of X rays is 3,000 times shorter than the mean wave length of visible light. The entire range stretches from 10^{-8} to 10^{-11} centimeters.

How does this mysterious radiation originate? If we direct a cathode ray (i.e., fast-moving electrons) at a solid object —say, a glass surface or a piece of metal—the motion of the electrons is suddenly braked. When this happens, the projectile gives up all its kinetic energy in a burst, but this is in no way lost, for it reappears as electromagnetic energy. The amount of energy involved remains about the same. For this reason a relatively slow electron produces only heat rays when its motion is arrested. The "brake energy" of a faster electron causes visible light to be emitted. If, however, the energy of the electrons is so great that electron shells close to the nucleus are affected, the shock of the brake on their motion gives rise to X rays.

Some of the shell electrons may be hurled out of their orbits and leave the atom. The process is tantamount to electrification or *ionization* of the atoms. The absence of electrons in the outer shell of the atom has the effect of making the ionized atom capture foreign electrons. On the other hand, the absence of electrons in the inner shells causes a much more far-reaching process. For a brief space it throws the whole electron architecture of the atoms into disorder. Just as the removal of a few bricks from the lower rows of a loosely laid wall will cause it to collapse, so the electrons in the outer shells fling themselves with elemental force into the vacant places in the inner shells. The energy so released produces quanta of light which in size are of the order of X rays of varying wave lengths and which are propagated at the speed of light. Of course, not every electron that hits the anticathode produces conditions of this kind. Only one electron in a thousand strikes so deeply into the atom that a collapse of the shells results. Nevertheless, it is estimated that in the case of a tube emitting one quadrillion electrons per second, a trillion of such energy-charged light quanta are smashed out of the atoms of the anticathode. But 99.5 to 99.9 per cent of the total energy supplied to an X-ray tube is converted into heat. Only 0.1 to 0.5 per cent appears in the form of the desired radiation. The result of these high temperatures is that the tube becomes exceedingly hot. Not infrequently the heat melts the metal anodes if they are not made of highly heat-resistant material.

Unfortunately, X rays, unlike light rays, cannot be focused at a point through specially constructed "lenses." To concentrate the rays in a small area to be irradiated—the only means of achieving the greatest sharpness of outline in X-ray photographs and in therapeutic use—the designer of such tubes must resort to special measures. He has created, for instance, the Pantix Revolving Anode Tube, which is very suitable for even the most difficult examinations. The anode, a thick circular disk, rotates at about 3,000 revolutions per minute. Alternatively, there are the minimum-focus tubes, in which the source of radiation is no bigger than 0.3 × 0.3 millimeters and so represents a virtual point source.

The Inner Rhythm of Atoms

Among the first casualties of the Gallipoli campaign of 1915 was a twenty-seven-year-old volunteer, a physicist from Oxford, Henry Gwyn Jeffreys Moseley. Just before the outbreak of the war he had come to the fore with work that provided evidence of a towering intellect and, in spite

of his untimely death, assured him a place in the ranks of the
great physicists.

In 1912 Ernest Rutherford, then director of the physics
laboratories at the University of Manchester, had assigned
to Moseley the task of examining the known elements by
means of X rays. The object was to establish from the diffraction patterns to what extent there were similarities
among the types of atoms. X rays seemed particularly suitable for the purpose because their wave lengths are some
3,000 times shorter than those of light rays. Only with such
short-wave light rays was there a hope of making measurements inside the atoms and discovering the governing laws.
To attempt the same task with ordinary light rays would be
comparable to an effort to find the exact diameter of a pin-
head with a ruler a yard long.

Young Moseley approached Rutherford's commission
with little enthusiasm. On several occasions he expressed
misgivings to his colleagues about the difficulties of the task.
What complicated his work particularly was the variety of
X rays. The X-ray tube he used did not produce a uniform
type of ray, but rather of a mixture of *soft* and *hard* rays.
Their varying power of penetration caused him a good deal
of trouble.

Max von Laue had proved that crystals irradiated with X
rays show excellent diffraction patterns that reveal their
lattice structure. They had brought the research scientists
enlightenment on the regular arrangement of atoms within
solid matter.

Now crystal lattices proved to be the only effective instrument for Moseley's project: with them he could realize
his idea of building an *X-ray spectroscope* that would work
like an ordinary light spectroscope. It was even possible to
adopt parts of a light spectroscope for the purpose. The
light source was replaced by an X-ray tube with a platinum
anticathode. Moseley tightly confined the radiation from

there by means of two screens. He directed the beams thus produced not onto a glass prism, as in a light spectroscope, but onto a crystal. It was diffracted by the lattice structure of the crystal and then guided onto an electric detector, whose purpose was to measure the strength of the X ray emerging from the crystal. Both crystal and detector were set up on swivel mountings on a common axis. By this means, X rays coming in from various angles could be compared with the emergent ray. In the course of his experiments Moseley noted that at certain angles the diffracted radiation came in at greater strength. This phenomenon was already known, and had been precisely described by William Henry Bragg and his son, William. But Moseley went a step further. He worked out the exact angles at which the X rays appeared at greater strength. He found that on the basis of these and the crystal constant—a value that was available for almost all crystals—the wave length of the incoming ray could be accurately determined. His investigations showed that his X-ray tube was emitting X rays of five different wave lengths. These X rays corresponded to five different color tones of light.

But it had been known, since Niels Bohr had formulated his theory of the atom, that light can arise only as a result of appropriate jumps by electrons inside an atom shell. As we have already said, Moseley's X-ray tube had a platinum anti-cathode. Where, therefore, could the radiation originate but in the platinum atoms? The radiation he had so carefully measured must be characteristic of, and peculiar to, platinum. But if there was a particular form of radiation for platinum, other elements, when used as anticathodes, must likewise give off radiation of their own. Moseley tested twelve elements for this property, among them iron, nickel, copper, cobalt, silver, and gold. With each substance he used as a screen to intercept the electrons from his X-ray tube, Moseley succeeded in tracking down the appropriate specific radiation. Each of the elements examined had one, and it was always made up of X rays of varying wave lengths.

In the meantime Moseley had improved his apparatus. He had replaced the not very reliable detector by a photographic plate that supplied him with a natural image of the X rays given off by the substances under study. Line spectra emerged which were in general similar to those of light. Among the individual lines to be seen, a number regularly stood out with greater prominence. Between the more prominent lines there was always a number of weaker ones in a group or series. The individual groups were separated by fairly large intervals. What seemed particularly remarkable to Moseley was the fact that as the atomic weight of the substances he was studying increased, the wave lengths of lines combined in a group became shorter. The atoms undoubtedly had a definite underlying structural rhythm that was manifested by the periodical recurrence of lines assembled in groups. In an effort to label the individual groups, he tagged them with letters. He identified the K, L, M, N, O, P, and Q groups.

Moseley found yet another important connecting link, again based on a regular feature of the line spectra. It was reflected in the wave lengths of X rays emitted by a particular element. If, by a specific formula, he assigned the figure Q to the wave length of the radiation given off by one of these elements, he found that Q increased by one each time he used as his anticathode a substance adjacent to its predecessor in the periodic table. The value increased by two if he used the next element but one. If, for instance, he had previously used iron as his anticathode and now chose copper, he found the value Q increased by three. Cobalt, which is next to iron in the periodic system, increased the value Q by only one, nickel by two. This systematic law could only mean that an elementary quantum was present in the atom which increased by one unit from element to element. In December 1913 he expressed the view that this elementary quantum could only be the electric charge on the central positive nucleus, the existence of which had been known for a long time.

In April 1914 he published a further report in which he supplemented his previous work with diagrams of the X-ray spectra of a total of forty-six elements. He emphasized that the relationships between the elements and the X rays expounded by him were applicable to all elements. Up to that time, elements had been arranged according to their mass. Hydrogen, being the lightest element, was No. 1. Next came helium as No. 2, and so on. However, Moseley's work proved that an element cannot be classified on the basis of its chemical mass, its weight, alone, but only by the number of protons present in the nucleus—the atomic number—and that in many cases the chemical mass plays a completely subordinate role and may often lead to misjudgments.

The chemists found in Moseley's results confirmation of their belief that the long-suspected numerical rhythm linking the elements was no mere figment of their imaginations, but to all appearances had its origin inside the atoms themselves. The atomic numbers worked out by Moseley were for the most part in harmony with the ordinal numbers of the periodic system. Where, in one case or another, agreement was not apparent, Moseley showed that the chemical mass—i.e., the weight of the element in question—had been wrongly calculated, or that variants of one and the same element, with different chemical masses, were involved.

Like Dmitri Ivanovich Mendeleev (1834–1907), the Russian chemist who had previously succeeded in predicting new elements merely by arranging the elements according to their atomic weights, Moseley now pointed to a number of empty spaces in his table which betrayed the existence of other elements.

He was not destined to see the day of their discovery. But he left a legacy to science which contained the key to a reconstruction of the atomic structure of the heavy elements. The line spectra of the individual elements photographed by him showed a striking similarity. The K group of iron corresponded in every particular to the K group of, say, nickel or copper. The same was true of the others—the L, M, and N groups, for instance. Now, analogous line spectra correspond to an analogous process among the electrons oscillating inside the atom, and analogous processes suggest that atoms have a uniform structure. "All this," wrote the German physicist Walter Kossel, "pointed clearly to the conclusion that we must view X-ray spectra as a manifestation of the internal behavior of atoms, coming from a depth to which external forces can penetrate only with difficulty, and at which all atoms of the various elements are similarly constructed."

The Shadow Play on the X-ray Screen

The power of penetration possessed by X rays varies according to the nature of the material. Elements with a high atomic weight form a greater obstacle than those with a low atomic weight. This property makes it possible for doctors to differentiate between bones and soft parts. Bones throw a dark shadow; skin and flesh, consisting for the most part of such lighter substances as carbon, hydrogen, and oxygen, scarcely obstruct the rays at all and are only faintly visible on the fluorescent screen.

Animal, human, and plant organisms do not present a uniform mass. The different densities of substances are naturally associated with different degrees of absorption. Accordingly, on the basis of the delicate shadows thrown by tissue, one organ can be distinguished from another. To the doctor who can "read" these shadows, the X-ray picture is an indispensable aid in diagnosis. Many diseases cause an alteration in the tissue. Where inflammation occurs, a swelling or reddening of the skin almost always appears, accom-

panied by pain. In an X-ray photograph, inflammation can
be recognized by the fact that inflamed portions of tissue
cast cloudier shadows than the healthy portions surrounding
them. Thus, a thickening with a discharge of pus, or any
other change produced by the tuberculosis bacillus in the
normally aerated tissues of the lung of a tubercular person,
shows up distinctly as a darker area in the X-ray photograph. The changes that occur during a healing process are
just as accurately identifiable as those in a diseased lung.
Even after years have passed, the healed portions of the lung
stand out clearly in an X-ray photograph and provide the
physician with information about the extent of illnesses that
have been overcome.

If the thorax is X-rayed from behind, the heart can be
clearly discerned next to the lung tissue. Being a particularly
thick, blood-rich muscle, it appears in the photograph as a
dark shadow. This makes it possible for enlargements, dila-
tions, displacements, and other disorders to be reliably diag-
nosed. In the case of hollow tissues that are less readily
visible, the doctor achieves the desired effect by filling them
with opaque materials. Contrast can be produced by pump-
ing a substance with a high atomic weight into cavities such
as the stomach or bladder. Sometimes denser substances
are used for the purpose, such as barium compounds for the
interior of hollow organs. In such cases the opaque meal
stands out in sharp relief, so that any change in the tissue can
be recognized. Changes such as bulges, constrictions, or
strangulations usually inform the doctor about the nature of
the illness, and so enable him to decide whether he is dealing,
for example, with cancerous symptoms or not. If the doctor
suspects an internal proliferation of cancer, he first fills the
cavity with opaque materials of a heavier type, then evacu-
ates it and pumps in air. The opaque residue remaining in
the cavity is deposited by the pressure on the inner wall of
the tissue, and provides a photograph that clearly re-

produces the outline of the hollow organ. By this means, growths on the inside of the intestinal walls can be detected, even when they have not caused constriction.

The shadow play on the X-ray screen also reveals foreign bodies; a chip of metal, a splinter, a bullet, or even a button that has been swallowed stands out distinctly against the paler tissue shadows.

In X-ray work three main methods of investigation are used: fluoroscopy, contact photography, and camera photography. In fluoroscopy the shadow of the X-ray picture is thrown on a fluorescent screen and studied by direct observation. In contact photography the fluorescent screen is replaced by a magazine containing photographic film. In the camera-photography method the screen is photographed from a certain distance so that a miniature picture of the X-ray shadow is obtained. Contact photography is used mainly in special clinical cases; camera photography is chiefly employed in mass X-ray examinations required in the fight against tuberculosis.

The Man Who Lost His Hair

In 1896 a young Viennese physician, Dr. Leopold Freund, read in an American newspaper a story about a technician whose hair had fallen out after he had worked for a lengthy period of time with X rays. Although much of what was written about X rays in those years soon proved to be fantasy, Dr. Freund decided to look into the scientific merits of that newspaper story.

Having applied in vain to several local institutions for permission to use their laboratories, he finally turned to the Graphische Versuchs- und Lehranstalt, an institute concerned with the graphic arts which was known in Vienna for the progressive spirit of its administration. Its director

gave Freund permission to work with the one available
X-ray tube in the building, and allotted him a workroom of
his own.

Dr. Freund's "guinea pig" was a little girl whose face was
disfigured by a mole with hair growing all over it. For ten
days he directed X rays on to this facial blemish, though
only for a few minutes each day. After several days the hair
began to fall out—where there had previously been a thick
hair growth, a circular patch of bare skin now appeared.
This test, as we know today, was the first proof of the
biological effectiveness of X rays. But when Dr. Freund told
a fellow physician about his observations, he earned anything but approval. Not until some years later, after several
technicians, doctors, and research scientists had suffered
severe injuries as a result of constantly handling X rays, did
people remember Freund, who had in the meantime quietly
continued his experiments. Now at last one of the clinics
connected with the University of Vienna placed a small par-
titioned area on a staircase landing at his disposal.

By this time the therapeutic use of X rays had been introduced in a small way; it was confined to the healing of stub-
born cases of infectious skin diseases, such as scald head,
barber's rash, and ringworm. From the start the greatest
difficulty had been how to decide the correct dosage.

Later, efforts were made to solve the problem of providing protection against the rays by tackling it from the
angle of the instruments. Tube radiation was developed,
then the "radiation gun," and finally the Siemens "X-ray
bomb," which encloses the parts (including the transform-
ers and high-voltage equipment) in one casing, all screened
except a tiny aperture from which the rays emerge. Even
this did not suffice to provide complete protection of the
medical personnel against X rays—which, moreover, were
constantly becoming stronger. It became evident that
through the use of high-voltage X-ray tubes and the very
hard rays generated by them, the body of the patient itself

became radiant during irradiation. The hard X rays were *scattered* over the body, thus exposing the doctor to a new danger. This scattered radiation could be strong enough to damage the blood and the gonads if the doctor giving the treatment were not very carefully protected.

This led to the invention of the *lead coffin*, in which the patient was laid while under radiation. In the end, the problem of providing complete protection for the doctor in charge was solved by putting him and his dosimeter in a special radiation-proof room from which X-ray treatment was conducted and observed through thick lead-glass windows.

Until 1901 virtually no method existed of making quantitative measurements of X rays. Then came the roentgenometer, to the great good fortune of the medical profession and, even more, of patients. How excessively dangerous and treacherous X rays can be in large doses— but also in tiny doses administered in unbroken succession —is shown by the long list of doctors, biologists, and technicians who, through constant handling of these rays, died an agonizing death, or who, as a result of serious burns, had to undergo amputations to save their lives. It was quickly found that lead-lined fabric afforded a certain degree of protection. This resulted in the development of protective articles of clothing such as lead-lined rubber coats, aprons, special gloves, and lead-glass goggles that are still in use. Once the great dangers were recognized, careless handling of X rays in laboratories and in sanitariums was swiftly brought to an end.

CHAPTER 7

From Natural
to Artificial Radioactivity

SINCE THE PUBLICATION of Röntgen's work, the question of the origin of X rays had become of paramount interest. It was still not known how this radiation with remarkable qualities was produced. Some physicists suspected that it was to be found in one of the active materials with which luminescent screens were treated. If this assumption was correct, they reasoned, then isolated luminescent substances —say, in the form of a mineral or salt—must also darken a photographic plate without the presence of an X-ray tube. The substances making up the luminous coatings of the luminescent screens used in those days were a matter of exact knowledge: they were, for the most part, uranium salts.

One of the scientists working along these lines was the Frenchman Antoine Henri Becquerel, son and grandson of physicists, a man in his mid-forties at that time. First Becquerel exposed the uranium salts to sunlight. Then he wrapped them in black paper and put them in a box, which he placed on a photographic plate. He conjectured that the rays he hoped to discover would pass through the black paper and affect the photographic film. After many disappointing experiments, the plates one day showed a darkening. Becquerel was firmly convinced that this was caused by the mysterious X rays—i.e., Röntgen rays. He assumed that a uranium salt—in this case, potassium uranium sulfate—emits X rays if previously exposed to sunlight.

Becquerel notified the French Academy of Sciences of his discovery on February 24, 1896. He was not to find out until later that his report to the Academy was wrong. It was not true that the uranium salts had been excited by sunlight to give off radiation, nor had any X rays darkened the photographic plate.

A mere accident made Becquerel aware of his error. He had put some boxes containing uranium salts wrapped in stout black paper in a drawer in which there were also some undeveloped photographic plates. He intended to use these to continue his experiments in stronger sunlight in the summer. However, on March 1, 1896, when Paris was already bathed in glorious spring sunshine, Becquerel decided to repeat his experiments. First he examined the photographic plates to make sure that they had not been darkened by the uranium salts lying near. He found that such darkening had in fact taken place. In the light of his communication to the Academy, this discovery was a painful one. He could find only one explanation: the uranium salts must, without needing stimulation by light, constantly emit some direct, penetrating rays.

The following day Becquerel advised the Academy of his new discovery in very restrained terms. "I can only surmise," he stated, "that we are dealing with a new kind of radiation, radiation apparently related to that which M. Röntgen has discovered at Würzburg. How do I arrive at this view? Like his, the radiation penetrates opaque bodies, and darkens a photographic plate when all light is switched off—

indeed, even when the plates are enclosed in a lightproof container with only a small amount of air space between them and the source of radiation. It also turns the air surrounding it into a conductor of electricity. In other words, it manifests all the same characteristics as Röntgen's X rays.

"Nevertheless," he continued, "I cannot make up my mind to regard it as identical with these, for its place of origin is not a tube of Röntgen's design, but simply, as already stated, uranium salts. I should like, therefore, merely to express the cautious surmise that the radiation I have found is not associated with such salts alone. Certainly, it seems so up to now."

Becquerel was right. The uranium salts were not the only source of these rays. The radiation coming from the salts was the weakest radiation of its kind. In fact, it was astonishing that Becquerel had been able to demonstrate its presence at all. By doing so, he had for the first time provided proof of the existence of radioactivity.

A Carload of Waste

It was soon established that the only substance in the salts which could be acting as the source of radiation was uranium. Uranium? What substances contained uranium? Where did they occur? The raw material was pitchblende, a by no means rare mineral. Many deposits in which uranium minerals were found along with silver existed in Bohemia, then part of the Hapsburg empire. It could be assumed that the origin of the radiation would be found not in the pitchblende itself but rather in the uranium, and perhaps even in other previously unknown substances as well.

The first efforts to analyze pitchblende were made by a young Polish woman from Warsaw who, having become involved in the students' revolutionary organization, had found it advisable to leave her native country, which then was under Russian rule. She had emigrated to Paris, where, living on a starvation diet, she had finished her studies at the Sorbonne. In her new task she had the advice and help of one of her former teachers, Pierre Curie—who soon became her husband.

The two researchers found that the residues of pitchblende, the substances and waste remaining after the uranium had been extracted, contained strong rays. Might they not give off radiation incomparably stronger than that given off by metallic uranium? Enormous quantities of such pitchblende residue were lying in the dumps of mineral waste at the government-owned silver mines of Joachimsthal in Bohemia. Up to that time no one had bothered about this apparently valueless material. To the mining authority it was merely a nuisance; in fact, plans were afoot to close the mines on account of the ever-mounting dumps, as well as the low yield of silver.

The Curies suggested that the Austrian mining authority be asked to hand over to them a few carloads of that waste for experimental purposes. The request was made, the Austrian government agreed, and one day a railroad car, its load duly declared as "waste," arrived in Paris. No one knew that it contained the most valuable metal in the world.

The small funds of the Curies had dwindled in the course of their earlier experiments. The labor of subjecting pitchblende to a wearisome process of fractionation was carried out with the most primitive equipment, such as electroscopes fashioned from empty tea cans. The Curies worked in a tumbledown shed; for a long time Mme Curie herself carried the large quantities of water that were needed, because there was no water piped in; and the roof was so dilapidated that the walls often ran with rain water.

Such were the conditions in which the first radioactive substance was extracted in 1898. The Curies called it *polonium* for Marie's homeland. This first attempt to isolate the metal had taken no less than forty-five months. Shortly afterward the Curies found a second and some time later a third radioactive substance. The second was named *radium* (Latin, *radiare* = to emit rays), and the third *actinium* (Latin, *activus* = active).

How extraordinarily laborious and costly a process the extraction of these substances was is shown by the fact that from ten tons of pitchblende residues, enough to fill an entire railroad car, only one gram of radium chloride—still by no means pure radium—was obtained. With the method of extraction in use at the time, that one gram cost $60,000. When the value of the new radioactive substances became known, there were beaming faces at the offices of the Austrian mining authority—all at once the bothersome Joachimsthal waste dumps were worth far more than the silver mines.

Immediately after the discovery of the new elements was announced, the Curies received a substantial stipend from the French government. In addition, they were awarded, jointly with Becquerel, the Nobel Prize for physics in 1903. On April 19, 1906, Pierre Curie, only forty-seven years old, was run over by a horse-drawn wagon when crossing a street and was killed on the spot. Marie Curie died on July 4, 1934, of aplastic pernicious anemia caused by her exposure to radium radiation over a period of decades.

Radium

Very soon after the preparation of radium compounds in the pure state was achieved, the discoverers were swamped with requests for minute quantities of a radium preparation. One of the men who actually received such a tiny quantity—in a small glass tube—was Ernest Rutherford.

Born in New Zealand in 1871, Rutherford had in 1898 been appointed professor of physics at McGill University in

Montreal; earlier he had done research under Joseph John Thomson at Cambridge. Having followed the Curies' and Becquerel's work with the greatest interest, Rutherford was already familiar with the radiation emitted by uranium. In the course of his own experiments he had encountered some remarkable phenomena that the radium substance from Paris enabled him to follow up more closely.

If, for example, radium were allowed to act on pure water, it became a conductor of electricity. Under the influence of radium, various substances gave off visible light. In darkness they became spontaneously luminescent. Radium chloride of 100-per-cent purity, when melted and therefore completely anhydrous, emitted an intensely blue light. In addition to barium cyanoplatinite and zinc blende, the mineral willemite showed a green fluorescence and kunzite a red fluorescence, while a diamond gave off a bluish light. Under the action of radium, too, the lens, the vitreous humor, and the retina of the eye began to glow. Colorless glass was tinted by it: sodium glass became violet, glass with an iron content became brown. Certain salts likewise acquired such colorations. Rock salt became yellow, and melted borax blue. The ability of metals to transmit the rays varied. Lead turned out to be the most obstructive: it provided an almost perfect screen against the rays. If a radium preparation was placed in a hole bored in a block of lead, the radiation could escape in only one direction. If, therefore, any kind of material was placed over the bore hole, the penetrating power of the rays could be tested.

During one of these experiments a remarkable thing was observed. If the flow of rays issuing from the bore hole was exposed to a strong electric field, the beam divided: one pencil was deflected toward the positive pole, the other to the negative pole; a third remained completely unaffected by the electric field. This meant that the polarity of the first pencil was negative, that of the second positive, while the third was of a wave character similar to that of light. But the degree of deflection yielded another conclusion. The radium preparation behaved like a cathode-ray tube to which a potential of more than 100,000 volts, an enormously high figure for the conditions then existing, had been applied. The electrons emerging traveled at a speed approaching 130,000 miles per second.

On the other hand, the preparation produced the effects of an X-ray tube. It supplied rays identical with X rays. They darkened a photographic plate and showed high penetrating power. But here, too, the X rays produced by normal means could not stand comparison with the present rays. The gamma rays from the radium preparation, though so similar to them in character, had a much shorter wave length, and were therefore incomparably *harder*. The final physical oddity was that, in addition to its other features, the preparation could be regarded as a source of *canal rays* because, like an appropriately constructed tube, it gave off radiation carrying a positive electric charge. But whereas the canal-ray tube merely delivered positive electric particles of the size of a hydrogen-atom nucleus, the present particles were considerably heavier. It turned out that one of these particles was approximately four times as heavy as an ordinary proton and weighed 7,400 times as much as an electron, besides carrying twice the positive electric charge. The velocity at which it traveled—about 10,000 miles per second—was far superior to that of normal canal rays.

Scientists called the three types of radiation alpha, beta, and gamma rays, simply using the three first letters of the Greek alphabet, just as Röntgen had labeled his radiation with one of the last three letters of the alphabet, the letter X.

Many degrees and honors were bestowed upon Rutherford in the course of his distinguished career, which led him to Manchester and back to Cambridge. He was awarded the Nobel Prize for chemistry in 1908, was knighted in 1914,

and was created a baron seventeen years later. Lord Rutherford died in Cambridge in 1937.

Radioactivity Is "Hereditary"

Uranium decays into radium, an element of a quite different character. And radium? In the course of time a whole
series of substances has been derived from this element, all
of them having the same "mother": uranium. Each of them
proves to be radioactive—that is, it emits radiation. The
series extends as far as lead, the element with which the decay suddenly ceases.

In 1902 Rutherford advanced the theory that the radioactivity of certain substances is nothing more than the
spontaneous decay of certain atoms, a decay that cannot be
affected by any chemical or physical disturbing influence.
The decay, he said, is accompanied by the emission of rays of
a material and electromagnetic nature, the atoms of one element being transformed into those of another and lighter
element.

Rarely has the scientific world been shaken by such a
storm as the one that followed the publication of Rutherford's theory. The statement meant that all knowledge
about the atom which had previously been regarded as certain was wrong, for up to that time the atom had been regarded as "indivisible and immutable." If the claims of
Rutherford and his collaborator, the chemist Frederick
Soddy, were correct, the whole laboriously constructed
theory of the atom fell to the ground.

Alongside this radioactive series, known as the *uranium
series*, the existence of two others was demonstrated, the
thorium and the *actinium* series: three great families in
which radioactivity is, as it were, a kind of "hereditary
disease." As in a long chain of ancestors, this "disease" is

passed down from one member to another. This uncanny transmission of decay, which for no apparent reason and seemingly without sense or purpose causes the dissolution of the innermost structure of atoms in the same way as cancer does with animal tissue, reveals the processes of birth and death in the individual elements. Here, apparently rigid matter breaks up quite spontaneously. The strict adherence to laws with which this decay takes place sets these substances apart from the rest of the known elements. In spite of this, they appear to be governed, as Rutherford put it, by "a principle of the natural process."

It has been calculated that a tiny pinch—a few milligrams —of radium can give off rays incessantly for 1,600 years, and even then the stock of rays is only half exhausted. After another 1,600 years it drops to a quarter, and 1,600 years later to an eighth. 16,000 years elapse before the degree of radioactivity is reduced to a thousandth part, and before the last ray leaves the preparation, millions of years pass into eternity. However, among the radioactive substances, there are other elements that "live" faster. The physicist or chemist who believes he has a particular substance in his hands discovers to his astonishment that it has long since changed into something else. Phantom particles? What else could they be when, like radium C', they are transformed in a hundred-thousandth part of a second from one element into another? With the passage of time we have learned a great deal about the *life period* of such elements, but there is no rule to be deduced about the individual ones. Those with a long life exist beside the short-lived. Elements with half-life periods—the time in which their activity declines by half—of millions of years are found alongside those which count them in years, days, minutes, seconds, or fractions of a second.

It has been found that substances with a long life give off weaker radiation. The short-lived elements are the most strongly radioactive. A gram of radium, an element with a half-life position approximately in the middle of this range, emits several billions of alpha particles per second. Radium C′ has proved to be powerfully radioactive. The effective range of its radiation is as long as three inches. What this means in the case of an object the size of an atomic nucleus can best be visualized from an example: to an atom a distance of three inches is the same as a range of 15 million miles to a rifle bullet. It is impossible to conjure up even an approximate mental picture of the power that would have to be generated to propel a bullet that far.

Cloud Tracks

In 1912 Charles Thomas Rees Wilson, a Scotsman, introduced to the public a physical apparatus with which he claimed to be able to observe the way rays given off by radioactive elements behave in a gas. This apparatus was given the mysterious name "cloud chamber." It consisted in essence of a glass container with a few ordinary tubes branching out of it, each provided with a faucet. It also contained a diaphragm. To prepare the apparatus for use, absolutely pure air containing water vapor was passed into the container, the internal pressure of which was then lowered. If at the same time alpha rays or beta rays were shot into the container, fine cloud tracks suddenly became visible precisely at the points where the rays entered. The cloud tracks were produced by the rays fired in. All that had happened was a demonstration of the old, familiar property possessed by alpha rays of ionizing molecules of air. On their way through the air they wrest electrons from the molecules or atoms of a gas, and in this way the molecules or atoms acquire an electric charge. In this state and under a certain pressure they are able to attract water vapor, and the result is the formation of cloud.

It was this principle that Wilson used to observe alpha

particles and beta particles along their path. Yet we have no
notion today of the difficulties the constructor encountered
during the development of this apparatus. Even when it was
already functioning well, troubles arose while he was taking
photographs. It became apparent that the cloud droplets increased in size too quickly after the rays had been shot in.
The consequence was that the rays following them continually caused fresh droplets to form, so that the photographs showed not a single track but an indecipherable mass
of cloud. To remedy this, Wilson touched off a strong
electric spark at the moment when the air was expanding in
the chamber. This spark was calculated to last long enough
to light up the cloud tracks for the time required. By 1922
automatic Wilson chambers could take up to 100 photographs a minute. 23,000 photographs showing a total of
415,000 alpha-ray tracks were necessary to obtain only eight
pictures of the atomic transmutation of nitrogen into oxygen, an experiment already pioneered by Rutherford.

Photographs of alpha rays all showed the same picture:
straight lines usually ending in a sharp little bend. This bend
occurs when alpha particles are heavily braked. Another
collision with a molecule throws them out of their straight
path. If a whole pencil of alpha rays is shot into a cloud
chamber, almost all of them are seen to be of equal length.
If the alpha rays originate from an ordinary radium preparation emitting rays that ionize the air for a distance of only
about 1½ inches, that stretch will embrace about 150,000
ionized gas molecules. In the case of radium C'—whose
alpha particles, as we know, ionize a distance of roughly
three inches—the number of electrified gas molecules has
been put at 232,000. 50,000 ions per centimeter (roughly
130,000 per inch) is taken as an average basis for calculation.
This high figure is due to the fact that each alpha ray ionizes
the molecules around it. The visible track in the cloud is
really a diminutive tube made up of many thousands of

cloud droplets, a tube that closes behind the alpha particle as soon as it has passed.

An altogether different picture is presented by photographs of beta rays. Being some 7,400 times lighter than alpha particles, they cannot cause such a great disturbance in a gas. Consequently, the ionization of air molecules is on a quite small scale. The basis of calculation is some 1,500 to 2,000 ionizations per centimeter (i.e., up to about 5,000 per inch). The tracks, very finely drawn, twist a good deal and usually follow an irregular course. The faster the beta ray is traveling when shot in, the fewer cloud droplets the photograph shows.

Nowadays the Wilson cloud chamber is mostly used in conjunction with a heavy magnet. This enables us to establish at once the kind of ray entering the chamber. Any ray can be instantly identified from the degree of deflection, the strength of the cloud track, and, above all, the direction in which it is deflected. By virtue of its positive charge, an alpha ray is deflected in the direction opposite to the direction of a beta ray, and because of its greater mass, an alpha ray makes a more powerful impact than a beta ray. If, as happened in 1932, radiation tracks appear in the cloud chamber which have exactly the same strength as beta rays but are deflected like alpha rays, a new particle is known to be involved. The latter case provides the best proof of the existence of positively charged particles of the mass of an electron. They are named *positrons* and recognized as elementary particles.

Alpha Rays and Beta Rays Can Be Counted

In the early years of radium research, scientists often wondered how to determine the number of particles shot off by a radioactive preparation. Now that we know that a laboratory specimen of average size emits up to 30 billion alpha particles per second, it seems to us a piece of presumption that such a question was ever seriously raised. It would have been easier to count the stars in the sky than to ascertain the number of these invisible radiation particles. But the question was asked—and answered.

At the beginning the fluorescent screen alone was used for counting purposes. The dots of light that flared up strongly on the screen were alpha particles. Dots that glowed weakly were probably beta particles. Counting particles by this method was a highly laborious proceeding.

However, as often before in the history of discovery, everyday processes supplied a solution. What is a lightning flash, a thunderstorm? Before a lightning discharge occurs, various processes take place in the atmosphere. A lightning flash does not come out of a clear blue sky. To begin with, the air must be strongly ionized. It becomes so by reason of the fact that on calm days the sun vaporizes the waters of the ocean more than usual. The sun's rays ionize the tiny water molecules that rise into the sky in denser and denser masses, causing clouds to form. The clouds thicken, become heavier, and take on a bluish-gray tinge. Countless electrically charged water molecules accumulate to build cloud formations weighing many tons and developing an ever more menacing charge. This charge cannot, of course, increase beyond a certain limit, a limit set by the air underneath the cloud, which is normally a good insulator.

Eventually, just as the water in an overfilled pot runs over, the insulating capacity of the air becomes insufficient to withstand the urge of the opposing electric charges to neutralize. The slightest excess of charge is then enough to bring about neutralization and thus set off a shattering flash of lightning.

The fact that the slightest touch is sufficient prompted the German physicist Hans Geiger to make an experiment. In a glass tube he placed a slightly opened, cylindrical piece of sheet metal and drew a fine wire through the middle of the tube. The cylinder was then charged with a high-voltage electromotive force until the point was reached at which a spark jumped between the wire and the cylinder. If he adjusted the voltage so precisely that the charge was just short of a flashover, and if he fired an alpha ray or even a beta ray into his tube, the flash occurred in exactly the same way as if he had raised the voltage.

But did any practical gain result from this discovery? After every flash produced by a single alpha particle, Geiger had to wait until the ionization level in the *tube counter* was restored. Four alpha particles a minute was all that could be achieved.

In collaboration with others, Hans Geiger pursued his experiments for fifteen years, until he was able to raise the rate of count virtually to infinity. Now, whenever a ray passes through the electrically charged chamber, be it a stray electron, an alpha particle, a beta particle, or one of the mysterious cosmic rays, the tube counter registers it and keeps a tally with uncanny precision and regularity.

Rutherford Fires Alpha Particles

Alpha particles had been known for about twenty years, without having been employed for any other purpose than making measurements, when Rutherford succeeded in using them to transform atoms.

Four valuable properties possessed by these alpha particles prompted him in 1919 to undertake his experiments. The first was their small dimensions; the nucleus had proved to be not much bigger than that of a proton. Also important were their relatively high velocity, calculated at about 12,-000 miles per second, and their fairly large mass, which had proved to be 7,400 times that of an electron. Finally, the fact that the alpha radiation constituted 98 per cent of the total radiation emitted by radium C′ put the alpha rays at the head of the list. It meant that they could be used in large quantities for direct bombardment.

However, it has to be borne in mind that Rutherford's alpha particles were not shot pellets that could be manipulated at will, and that the radium C' preparation he used because its radiation was effective up to a range of three inches was not an inexhaustible arsenal of power. The question therefore arose whether the energy from such alpha particles would suffice to influence an atomic nucleus. Rutherford regarded this as probable. Specifically, he asked himself to what centigrade temperature a simple helium nucleus—and the alpha particle is nothing else—would have to be heated in order to raise its velocity from three fourths of a mile per second to 12,000 miles per second. According to his calculations, the temperature required was of the order of 30 billion degrees centigrade. He further asked himself what would happen if a gas were heated to such a temperature. He knew that this procedure would not only strip off all the electrons, but presumably would powerfully affect the atomic nuclei as well.

Fortunately, Rutherford did not have to generate such a temperature. The radium C' preparation supplied him with atomic missiles without being heated—indeed, without any action at all on his part. His experiments at first met with little success. Among the trillions of nitrogen atoms that were bombarded with alpha rays, there were only a few that could be presumed to have been transformed into oxygen atoms. Rutherford's experimental apparatus consisted of a glass receptacle containing pure nitrogen and a radium C' preparation, plus a simple fluorescent screen that was movable.

How was Rutherford to ascertain that a transformation had actually taken place? He knew, for example, that the extreme range of his alpha particles was roughly three inches. If he adjusted the position of the screen to this distance, he saw dots of light appear upon it. He thereupon moved the screen away until the light vanished—i.e., until the screen was outside the effective range of the alpha rays. If now, he concluded, at some time somewhere on the screen's surface a flash was noted, this could only be due to the fact that a nuclear component, a proton, had been shot out of the nitrogen nucleus by an accidental direct hit while the alpha nucleus was left embedded in it. As the nitrogen nucleus contains seven protons (positively charged nuclear particles) and as the two protons of the alpha particle were now added to these while one proton was shot out, this yielded a figure of eight protons, a nuclear charge number appropriate to the atomic nucleus of oxygen. Such a flash was, in fact, detected on the screen from time to time— which proved that transformation had been accomplished.

Shortly after his successful attack on the fortress of the atomic nucleus, Rutherford wrote that it must be assumed that as a result of the enormous forces released when alpha particles collide with atoms of nitrogen, the nucleus of this atom is so affected that it loses one of its nuclear building blocks. All the indications were, he said, that the spot of light appearing on the screen was caused by a nuclear particle of the nitrogen atom. After the successful transformation of nitrogen into oxygen, it was possible by 1928 to transform no fewer than twenty-seven other substances by bombarding them with alpha particles. Some dozen of these transformations were achieved by P. Kirsch and G. Pettersson, two scientists working in Vienna.

Artificial Radioactivity

Anybody who takes only a fleeting look at a table of elements will see that among the non-radioactive elements there are only a few with integral atomic weights. We now know that all the non-radioactive elements are isotope mixtures. They are made up of atoms of the same kind, the only difference between these elements being that some are lighter than others. Carbon, with an atomic weight of 12.01, for example, consists of isotopes with atomic weights of 12 and 13. In the mixture of the two isotopes, the one with the atomic weight of 12 accounts for ninety-nine per cent, while the one with the atomic weight of 13 constitutes only one per cent. We know some elements, however, that possess as many as eleven isotopes. If we examine the atomic nuclei of such isotopes, we discover that the number of protons (positively charged heavy nuclear particles) is constant and that only the number of the neutrons (electrically neutral particles) fluctuates.

The neutron is a nuclear component, just as the proton is, and both together determine the atomic weight. The atomic nucleus, that minute structure occupying a fraction of one quadrillionth of the volume of the atom, is the home of the proton and the neutron. The nucleus of the helium atom contains two neutrons as well as its two protons. Many other atomic nuclei also contain neutrons and protons, usually in the proportion of 1:1. In the case of heavy nuclei, however, the number of neutrons is preponderant. Another exception is the case of the isotopes, which possess either more or fewer neutrons than protons. We know only one element—ordinary hydrogen—that normally contains no neutrons at all. In the heaviest element, uranium, the number of neutrons is the greater. Looked at purely from the point of view of weight, a ten-pound cube of uranium is composed of 3.86 pounds of protons and 6.14 pounds of neutrons. We are in a position to prepare isotopes of the same element synthetically by removing or adding neutrons. The formula for making and activating such isotopes was evolved by Frédéric Joliot and his wife, Irène Joliot-Curie, the daughter of the discoverers of radium. The famous Joliot team demonstrated that virtually any substance can be made artificially radioactive.

Early in 1934 they started out by continuing the experiments in which light elements such as boron, magnesium, and aluminum were bombarded, for the purpose of transformation, with alpha particles from a radium preparation. The quantity of radium at their disposal was relatively large. Following the changes set in motion by the hail of alpha projectiles, they found that rays that could definitely be identified as neutrons and atomic nuclei of hydrogen were emitted from time to time by the bombarded substances. What particularly riveted their attention was a strange phenomenon: the substances continued to give off rays even after the radium preparation, the nuclear gun, had been removed.

What had occurred in these experiments was nothing less than the conversion of non-radioactive into radioactive substances. To prove this was not difficult. The researchers merely had to place the bombarded elements near a luminescent screen to find that emission of rays often continued for ten, twenty, or even thirty minutes and longer. After that, in obedience to the same laws that govern radiation from *natural* radioactive elements, the radiation died down. Was it a fact that the materials thus stimulated by irradiation to spontaneous radiation had become new, previously unknown elements? The Joliot-Curies were soon able to answer this question. They had succeeded by complicated methods in achieving perfect separation of the sources of artificial radiation from the other substances. The scientific world heard with amazement the news about "artificially" activated forms of ordinary elements. On January 15, 1934, the Joliot-Curies notified the French Academy of Sciences of their discovery. Their report said: "By the use of outside agencies, we have succeeded in producing 'artificial' radioactivity in atomic nuclei."

Barely three months after the sensational announcement by the Joliot-Curies, a paper by the Italian Enrico Fermi appeared in the British scientific periodical *Nature* confirming the existence of "artificial radioactivity." Fermi pointed out that the alpha rays employed by the Joliot-Curies were not needed to create this, for the same effect could be achieved with neutrons. He stated that a whole series of elements had been excited to give off radiation by this means. "With the aid of neutrons," Fermi wrote, "almost any element can be made artificially radioactive. In this process, its nuclear-charge number, or in other words its atomic number, does not play any part at all." As his source of neutrons he had used a mixture of radon (radioactive gas) and beryllium powder. In the course of these experiments he made an additional discovery: if *slow* neutrons were employed, it was very often possible to achieve a strengthening of the artificial activation.

It became apparent that slow neutrons were more easily absorbed by atomic nuclei than fast neutrons. Fermi's explanation was that the nucleus of an atom behaves toward slow neutrons in a manner comparable to that of a ball of clay which is penetrated by a hailstone. If the latter is traveling at a moderate velocity, it will remain stuck in the ball. Applied to the atom, this process means that a moderately accelerated neutron is absorbed by the atomic nucleus, and that the atom is thereby made heavier. Its inner equilibrium is upset, and conditions in the nucleus become very unstable. The radioactivity generated acts as a safety valve to enable it to revert to its stable state. The unstable atom goes on giving off radiation in stages until it has become stable again. This may take seconds, fractions of seconds, minutes, days, years, or even tens of thousands of years.

What practical consequences resulted from the discovery of artificial radioactivity? First, it was possible to make stable elements radioactive. Through the medium of transformation, entirely new substances could be created, substances that either do not occur in nature or are only rarely found in the natural state. Lastly, the radioactivity emanating from these substances could be used in exactly the same way as that emitted by natural radium preparations.

Through a constant succession of new experiments of this kind throughout the world, the number of newly discovered types of atom and their isotopes was substantially increased. By the end of 1938 some 494 different types of atom were known. Of these, about 274 proved to be stable, 40 were naturally radioactive, and 180 artificially so. At present approximately 50 types of atom are known to occur naturally in the radioactive state. In addition, in the course of the last seventeen years, 420 new radioactive elements have been successfully prepared by artificial means. All these taken together produce a figure of 900 different types of atom, distributed over 101 places in the periodic system.

Until 1940 radioactive isotopes were prepared mainly by irradiating substances with deuterons (heavy hydrogen) in cyclotrons. Now the source from which artificially activated materials are regularly obtained is the atomic reactor or uranium pile. Like a baker with his dough, the physicist of today puts the objects he wishes to make radioactive in the atomic reactor and "bakes" them for periods of varying length. When he removes them, they are in a highly radioactive condition.

"Tagged" Atoms

Our earth is made up of ninety-two natural elements. Among them, carbon plays a special role. The "king of elements," it is the key ingredient in all organic chemical compounds. But the importance of carbon is not confined to its having a vital share in the structure of all living matter. By virtue of its well-nigh unlimited capacity for forming combinations, it supplies the bulk of all chemical compounds. Carbon combines with practically all elements. As against the 20,000 to 40,000 compounds that all other elements together can form, there are at the present moment more than 400,000 carbon compounds. In most compounds carbon appears as the key element. Nevertheless, we have only a very imprecise conception of the role it plays in these compounds.

This is particularly true where clinical pictures of disease are concerned. It is therefore the constant endeavor of scientists to ascertain the carbon content in healthy and sick tissue. Their aim is to find out the part played by carbon when the body is healthy and when it is sick. The procedure used is to mix radioactive carbon in food. The radioactive atoms make their way into the body in company with the non-radioactive ones and function there as atomic "tracer ammunition," so to speak. The Geiger counter enables the researchers to follow the progress of these tracer elements even if only very few atoms are involved.

To the medical man they are an almost indispensable tool. He can closely follow the course and effect of a great variety of medicines, and with dosages that would make chemical analysis impossible. Even the weakest radiation from a radioactive substance can be detected with certainty. First an effort is made to discover how much of a substance entering the system through the medium of a medical preparation is afterward excreted. The residue remaining in the body is then easy to calculate. The next step is to locate the organs in which the preparation is present in concentrated amounts. This tells the doctor whether it has reached the areas where its effects are to be exerted. Finally, a general examination of various parts of the body and organs informs him how much of the preparation is to be found in each of them. For example, by examining a minute splinter of cancerous bone, a portion of cancerous tissue, a small piece of skin or even a hair or a fingernail clipping, a doctor can obtain an over-all view of the distribution of the preparation and of all those substances that a human being takes in with his food. He can thus judge whether diseased parts of the body are absorbing more than the normal amount of this or that element, or whether certain substances are being rejected by them.

·   ·   ·

The thyroid gland shows a definite susceptibility to iodine, while our bones react in the same way to phosphorus, and the blood to iron. With the help of radioactive iron, for instance, it is possible to determine the time it takes for red blood corpuscles to be formed in the bone marrow. The same tracer can be used to find out how iron taken in with food is stored by the body. By the same method we can establish when and by what route iron enters the blood in the event of a decline in the iron reserve in the blood. Similarly, the process by which oxygen reacts with protein-iron compounds can be observed. Such information provides the doctor and the research scientist with essential pointers for combating various diseases of the blood. In one case, interest will be concentrated on the carbon content of the bones and teeth, in another it will be concerned merely with the utilization of fat in tissue. It has been shown, for example, that new fat formed in a famished body is just as likely to be attacked as old fat accumulated over a period. By the use of nitrogen isotopes as tracers it has been possible to build up a good deal of evidence about the conversion of protein into living tissue. These days, moreover, even bacteria can be so "infected" with radioactive elements that they become, as it were, live tracers. They thus place in our hands a means of following the progress and the spread of an infection in precise detail.

Tagging of already well-tried remedies is of vital importance to research workers. This procedure enables them to find out how medicines counteract the propagation of certain harmful microbes, and in what period. Parallel observations are, of course, made to discover whether a medicine directed at a particular kind of bacteria may not damage other useful microbes. This is highly important because such damage may prevent the production in the intestine of necessary vitamins, which, as we now know, is frequently the work of bacteria. Injury to these vitamin-producing bacteria must be avoided at all costs. In all these cases the radioactive tracers occurring as fission products when atomic energy is generated are of inestimable value.

Protection against Radiation

One day in 1899 Mme Curie presented Antoine Henri Becquerel with a small specimen of a radioactive salt sealed up in a tiny glass tube. Becquerel put the tube in the vest pocket in which he kept his watch. He carried the tube around with him for weeks and forgot all about it. One day he felt pain in the area and noted that a red mark had appeared on his skin. Soon the pain—directly under the place where he carried his watch—grew more and more intense. Examining the vest pocket and finding the little tube again, he realized at once that the pain in that neighborhood must have been caused by the radiation coming from the tube. He reported this to Pierre Curie, Marie's husband, who, doubting Becquerel's assumption, promptly decided to perform an experiment on himself. He bound a small tube containing the same solution to his lower arm and went around wearing this odd bandage. After a few days the skin under it began to hurt, and a short time later a red mark appeared there.

The radiation emitted by the radium preparation in Becquerel's pocket had in fact caused the injury to his skin. Millions of cells had been killed—burned, that is—although the radium preparation had been heavily diluted. In time even weak radiation can produce severe damage or have fatal effects.

It was the cumulative effect of minute quantities of radioactivity that killed Marie Curie and probably Mme Joliot-Curie, her daughter, as well as many other physicists and doctors. Many were so severely injured that they had to undergo several operations to escape with their lives. Most of them died as a result of constant contact with radioactive preparations, or through regular exposure to X rays, though often only to such small amounts of them as doctors and nurses are constantly receiving. Severe injury through radiation was suffered by the twenty-three Japanese fishermen on board the *Fukuryu Maru* when a rain of radioactive ash descended on them; it came from a hydrogen bomb that had been exploded over an atoll far away.

Rays are insidious. They may be there without our having the slightest indication of their presence. They shoot through us without causing the slightest sensation.

What, then, are rays? They may be fast-moving nuclear constituents of atomic nuclei which, like tiny machine-gun bullets, penetrate our bodies or burst through them. Those which are associated with physical things, such as the nuclear components of atoms, are called *corpuscular rays*. But rays are not always connected with physical particles. Most of the rays we know—heat rays, light rays, ultraviolet rays, X rays, gamma rays, radio waves—are electromagnetic waves. What is the effective mechanism of rays based on? In what way do they act upon us, and how are we injured by them?

We can shoot at sparrows with a cannon or fire at an elephant with a shotgun. The case of rays is very similar. They may come at us with the killing force of a cannon ball, or as gently as a soft breath of wind which barely affects us, depending on the kind of radiation, the period of its action, and its intensity. These factors interfere with the electrical processes in the tissue cells. On these processes the life in our cells depends. When the body cells breathe, when they burn foodstuffs, when they divide and multiply, when they build up catalyzing or protective substances, when they fight against outside influences or disease germs—in the final analysis, it is always electrical forces that set these functions in motion and maintain them. A cell without electrical impulses is dead.

The chemistry of the cell can be crippled, accelerated, or completely paralyzed. Basically, however, this chemistry is only an effect of the electrical forces in certain of the cell's building blocks. Therefore, crippling the chemistry of a cell means limiting or stopping altogether the exchange of electricity between the individual building blocks. That is what rays do as soon as they penetrate a cell. According to their nature and strength, they upset its electrical processes. This may cause electrons to be detached. The result is that individual building blocks of the cell fall out of their framework. This in turn involves the decay of cell matter. Or the chemistry of the cell may be so accelerated that the mechanism races like the runaway wheel of a watch—what was previously produced by the cell in thirty minutes is now manufactured in a matter of seconds.

Alternatively, radiation may paralyze the entire chemistry of the cell. The cell is then incapable of movement, and is no longer productive. If this condition continues for any length of time, the cell ultimately stifles. A direct hit in the command center eliminates the central direction, and then the cell is dead. The most common reaction is, however, that the cell processes are switched into high gear. This means that everything going on in the cell proceeds at a faster rate; it means that the process of metabolism is stepped up; active substances designed to counteract this are expelled; there is more breathing, and this in turn generates more heat, causing dilatation of the blood vessels and reddening of the skin. The doctor then diagnoses "burning caused by radiation."

Now, there are cells and cells. Among them there are giants and dwarfs, weaklings and athletes, manufacturers and ordinary workers, dictators and domestics. Some are addicted to dieting, others to gluttony; some are heat-producers, some light-absorbers, some are pain-suffering ascetics. Many other "specialists" exist.

The germ cells have a place of their own. In these small organisms everything needed to make a human being is found in the most perfect state of readiness: a work of art

whose component blocks permit of millions and millions of possibilities. However, a complicated structure, great or small, is always very delicate, and this is true of germ cells. Even a trifling amount of radiation can have extremely harmful effects. In these cells a dose that would leave others unperturbed is sufficient to touch off violent reactions. As in the germ cells, above all, every building block down to the smallest has an important function to perform in the body of the human-being-to-be, any damage resulting from radiation may have catastrophic consequences. It may lead to monstrosities, to giantism, or to deformities in individual limbs. In fact, entire organs or members may be absent. The germ matter may be so gravely affected that cells die. If this happens, the human being concerned is no longer capable of reproduction. A committee set up by the British Government in 1956 recommended that in the first thirty years of life no human being should accumulate more than 50 roentgen units of radiation from man-made sources such as X-ray apparatus, atomic reactors, or fallout occasioned by nuclear-weapons tests.

What are the realities of the case? There are, to begin with, the cosmic rays coming in from outer space, and the radiation caused by the natural radioactivity of the earth and the air. Their intensity can be very precisely measured. If we calculate this for a period of thirty years, we find that in that time a human being absorbs an amount of radiation no greater than 4.3 to 5.5 roentgen units.

When a man has his chest X-rayed, he takes in an average of 0.1 of a roentgen unit. If he were to have his chest X-rayed once a year for twenty-five years, he would receive between 2.5 and 3 units. To these must be added the tiny quantities of radiation which we absorb when we have shoes fitted or when we sit before our television sets, whose tubes give off very soft X rays. It is estimated that over a period of thirty years a man absorbs about 3 roentgens from such sources. If we put these quantities together, the

average dose taken in during that time already amounts to something in the neighborhood of 33 roentgens.

Unfortunately, in the recent past this has been supplemented by an extra dose of radiation in the form of radioactive fallout resulting from the explosion of nuclear weapons. If these tests are continued, we may expect that in the course of another thirty years humanity will be exposed to an additional dose of 0.25 to 0.5 roentgens. But the roentgen account can also be overdrawn in other ways. In the same period the radioactivity from the luminous face of a wrist watch, for example, contributes a dose of 0.25. If we take into account the clock faces with radioactive luminous figures to be found in any household, another 0.5 to 1 roentgen will easily be added. A person particularly exposed to danger in this respect is the aircraft pilot, who sits in front of dozens of luminous dials. In thirty years of professional activity he may receive a dose of 10 roentgens.

We can see that a human being may easily reach the danger level without being subjected to any radiation for medical purposes. But if he is X-rayed for a stomach ailment, for instance, he may take in on one occasion the amount of radiation he would normally receive over the whole thirty-year period. It has to be taken into consideration, however, that this constitutes irradiation of one area, and not of the whole body. If these examinations are repeated several times, the dose received may quickly mount to 100 roentgens and more: an extremely dangerous level. As long as the dosage is confined to very small areas of the body—as in cancer treatment, which involves only a few square inches of skin—a human being can "tolerate" 6,000 to 8,000 roentgens. But it is quite another matter when a tenth or even a twentieth of this dose is uniformly distributed over the body. In that event the person concerned is beyond aid.

Some professions particularly expose people to the dangers of radiation. X-ray technicians, doctors, nurses, isotope-laboratory technicians, and workers in atomic-energy

establishments are affected above all. Legally, such people may work only in protective clothing, and may not be exposed to more than 50 roentgen units in the course of thirty years.

If we bear in mind that the human germ cells cannot tolerate even 0.025 roentgens per week over a long period, the great danger represented by larger amounts is manifest. It does not matter in the least whether the dose of 0.025 roentgens per week is administered all at once or in "installments," for the quantities accumulate. Any amount of radiation, no matter how small, can affect the carriers of certain hereditary factors; and the more often the reproductive organs are exposed to radiation, the more probable the development of mutations becomes.

Yet another danger threatens us in the form of radioactive substances that are precipitated by rain and enter our bodies in one way or another. The radioactivity of the individual substances is sometimes not in itself a cause for concern. Nevertheless, these radioactive atoms may cause much greater damage than might generally be expected. Let us assume, for example, that our bodies, or any cells in the body tissue, absorb radioactive oxygen. The individual cell treats this oxygen in exactly the same way as the non-radioactive type, lodging the atoms in the places provided for them. The fact that these oxygen atoms are radioactive does not at first disturb the cell. That it has been placed in an extremely dangerous situation by the radioactive oxygen atom does not become apparent until later. Radioactive or not, the oxygen in the place allotted to it by the cell has an important function to perform. But whereas the stable oxygen always remains oxygen, this is not true of radioactive oxygen. After a certain time, it is transformed into a substance bearing absolutely no resemblance to oxygen: oxygen breaks down into nitrogen.

A nitrogen atom has quite different chemical properties, and consequently produces other effects in the cell. To the cell, nitrogen in place of oxygen means death. Previously very lively, the cell now languishes and is doomed. A short time ago various newspapers printed an appalling example of physical decay caused in this manner. It was a photograph of a young woman who had survived an atom-bomb attack, but had then aged beyond recognition in a matter of days. Up to now this danger to the cells has received scant attention. It is, in fact, not merely radiation that can injure us: this transmutation of the elements creates catastrophic consequences.

Uranium-graphite piles or heavy-water reactors cannot supply energy indefinitely. One day their output drops. The reason is that the reactor is clogged. When a nucleus of uranium 235 is split, it gives rise to two fragmentary nuclei. What was previously one nucleus of uranium 235 now becomes two lighter, but nevertheless complete, atomic nuclei. A chain reaction can be maintained only if the mass of uranium 235 is appropriately large. Thousands and thousands of billions of nuclei are split every second, so that in time the mass of uranium is appreciably reduced. Concurrently, the metal becomes markedly contaminated through the accumulation of impurity atoms, and the process of fission is impeded. Finally, when the degree of impurity has become too high, the process is halted altogether.

For this reason thorough removal of waste is necessary. The uranium has to be taken out of the pile. If the material concerned is uranium 238 enriched with uranium 235, both isotopes are produced together in the process of chemical decomposition. This metal can be used again, and plutonium then appears, which, like uranium 235, is fissionable. Plutonium, too, can be employed over again for building a uranium pile. The final residue is composed of some thirty to fifty different types of atom, which, however, occur in only small quantities and are only partially usable. All these products of fission are highly radioactive and are dangerous to human beings. Their radioactivity disappears only by degrees. In one material it will last long, in another the period of decay is shorter. The time involved fluctuates between a millionth part of a second and billions of years. In this context it is worth noting that the total energy of the radiation emitted by all radioactive substances is of the same order of magnitude. This means that substances with a short half-life period emit stronger radiation than those with a long half-life. Accordingly, a short-lived radioactive substance may in certain circumstances be more dangerous than one with a long life. An example of this is ordinary uranium itself. Its radiation is so weak that it can be safely picked up in the hand without the danger that the handling of radium would involve. Uranium, in fact, has a half-life period of some billions of years. Radium, with a half-life of 1,600 years, gives off radiation millions of times more powerful.

Whenever products of fission are separated out, small quantities of radioactive substances find their way into the water used and contaminate it. In appearance and taste, the water is indistinguishable from uncontaminated water. Such waste water should, of course, never be piped away into drainage systems or rivers. It is also dangerous to allow it to drain away into the earth, for then the contaminated water is either absorbed by plants or finds its way down to ground water. As plants serve as food for animals and ground water is in many cases the source of our water supplies, such carelessness would directly threaten man and beast. Let us look at an example of this.

In 1944, when vast areas of New Mexico were commandeered for the atom-bomb project and the evacuation of the population was begun, one old Indian refused to abandon his homestead; decades before, his tribe had been granted the right to fish in the nearby river. The authorities were adamant on his having to vacate his house, but allowed him to stay near his fishing grounds if he chose a place lower down the river. For a long time nothing more was heard of the Indian until one day the Bureau of Indian Affairs received a letter in which the man, reporting that he had not set eyes on a single living fish for weeks in the river, requested that he be allotted new fishing grounds. When the case was looked into, the river was found to be contaminated with radioactivity; weak as it was in intensity, it had been strong enough to wipe out the entire stock of fish. The radioactivity came from waste products of the reactor built on the riverbank nearby. The waste had first been kept in a clearing tank for a long time; but when most of it had decayed, it had been heavily diluted with water and piped into the river. In spite of all precautions, the liquid had retained sufficient radioactivity to wipe out the fish.

From then on, the Atomic Energy Commission realized that keeping watch on the reactor premises and establishments was not enough. It was also essential to maintain constant checks on the air and the nation's waters.

The active portion of a uranium-graphite or heavy-water reactor not only supplies energy in the form of heat but also gives off a relatively large amount of energy in the form of short-wave rays. Furthermore, some of the products of fission formed inside the reactor are very penetrating and diffuse out, causing additional contamination of the air. Of course, the quantities of this radioactive material are often quite small. But that is of little importance, because what matters is how much of them the body absorbs and how much of an affinity it has for such substances. Thus, our muscular tissue absorbs 30 per cent of the radioactive caesium received, 7.5 of the radioactive strontium, and 6 per cent of the barium, while the kidneys pick up 1.5 per cent of the radioactive tellurium. The thyroid gland absorbs up to 20 per cent of the iodine entering the body.

All these substances act on their surroundings with energies of 0.3 to 5.1 million electron volts. In addition to this, they are excreted very slowly from the body. It takes half the yttrium isotope Y-90 2,700 days to leave the body. Others, such as strontium 90 and caesium 137 and carbon 14, remain in the body for a long time. It is, of course, important to know the highest concentration that a human being can absorb short of the actual danger point. Sometimes this figure is very low. In the case of radioactive yttrium 91, the permissible content per cubic centimeter of air may not be more than 9×10^{-9} microcuries (μc). The concentration of radioactive strontium 90 may not exceed $2 \times 10^{-10} \mu c/cm^3$. With ruthenium 103, which collects in the kidneys, the allowable concentration is $3 \times 10^{-8} \mu c/cm^3$. Tellurium 129, on the other hand, which is likewise absorbed by the kidneys, becomes injurious as soon as the limit of $4 \times 10^{-8} \mu c/cm^3$ is passed.

The human body reacts just as sensitively to radioactive iodine. The permitted maximum is $6 \times 10^{-9} \mu c$/per cubic centimeter of air breathed. This applies to iodine with an atomic weight of 131. As against this, the element praseodymium, which is precipitated in the bones, can be absorbed to the amount of 2×10^{-7} microcuries per cubic centimeter of air breathed without causing harmful effects. Radioactive strontium 90, which is produced in quantity during uranium fission, is, along with cobalt 60, one of the most dangerous radioactive substances. It accumulates in the bone tissue, and observation has shown that its radiation can cause tumors there.

The concentration of radioactive products of fission in the air is increasing. The air in and around atomic-energy plants is examined day by day. So, of course, are the clothing and the skin of the workers. As they leave the plant, Geiger counters indicate whether their clothes contain traces of radioactive substances.

Every atomic reactor is enclosed in a thick protective casing of high-grade steel and another one of concrete several yards thick. This protective shield is designed to bring the rays to a dead stop in the steel, the concrete, or thick belts of water—i.e., to deprive them of their velocity. Only when they have been absorbed, or slowed down to the point where their velocity no longer differs from that of normal air molecules, can they be regarded as relatively undangerous. Nevertheless, there is still the danger that the rays may diffuse out.

The windowless room in which the atomic reactor stands can be entered only through reinforced concrete doors about a yard thick. If anyone were rash enough to enter this room without protective equipment, the penalty would be terrible radiation burns and an agonizing death by poisoning. After a brief spell in the reactor room, vomiting would set in, and the mucous membranes of the nose and intestines would begin to bleed; later the skin would turn a lobster red and develop ulcers with a malodorous discharge, accompanied by a high temperature; death would bring release after two or three days.

The remains of a person killed in that horrible manner would have to be enclosed in a thick sheath of concrete and buried in special ground; having been radioactive while still alive, the victim would continue to be so in death. Radiation would come from his body until the last vestige of it had decomposed.

Of course it is sometimes necessary for someone to enter the room in which the atomic reactor stands. This need arises, for instance, when an important part of the reactor has become defective.

Before anyone ventures into the room, the degree of radioactivity is measured. Then the probable duration of the planned activity is worked out with the aid of a model. The necessary number of steps is calculated, and allowance is made for any incident such as a stumble. Let us assume that the calculated duration of a particular job is thirty minutes, whereas the period for which a man in protective garments can remain unharmed is, under prevailing conditions, thirty seconds. Sixty men then would be required

to complete the job. A whistle signals the beginning and
end of each man's activity; once the stop signal is sounded,
no worker even gives a screw one extra turn; each man
begins his work at the point where the last man has left off.
Not every qualified craftsman and specialist is suitable for
this kind of work; what is required is not the go-getter,
but the man who is assured, calm and prudent in his approach to the work, and unlikely to forget the danger for a
moment.

However, radioactivity infects not only human beings
but also inanimate objects. "Do not pick anything up,"
"Do not touch anything," "Pass quickly here," "Do not
loiter here": these and similar notices are posted at atomic-
reactor plants. What is to be done with such "hot" gear in
case of damage? It is, of course, possible to encase the hot
gear in concrete blocks and sink them in a lake or in the
ocean.[1] But concrete might develop cracks and be penetrated by algae and plankton. By these, in turn, fish could
be contaminated.

Let us, moreover, bear in mind the size of an atomic-
power plant and think of the number of faulty tools and
defective objects that accumulate even in an ordinary
factory. And what is to be done with the quantities of radioactive ash? What of the products of fission which cannot be
used for industrial and medical purposes? Where are they
to go?

Until about thirty years ago the quantity of radioactive
substances possessed by the entire human race amounted to
no more than 1½ to 2¼ pounds, and this was distributed
among thousands of clinics and research institutions. Before long, plants manufacturing atomic products may have
several tons of these on their hands; but man is inventive
and likely to succeed in his efforts to treat these quantities
with as much care as the radium preparations.

---

[1] Opposition to offshore dumping of radioactive waste has increased
during the past few years, and the public-health authorities in most
countries are much concerned about the problem. (Translator's note)

CHAPTER 8

From the Spark Gap
to the
High-power Transmitter

RADIO WAVES are as old as time, but man was relatively late in discovering them. Every lightning flash, every spark, every glowing match and candle flame sends out electromagnetic waves. They are identical with the waves "artificially" produced in electric spark gaps or oscillators.

The existence of radio waves has been known for about seventy years. Through radio broadcasting in the past thirty-five years, and in the past fifteen years through television, they have become the common property of the nations. Now life among civilized people is unthinkable without radio and television. Electric waves have become aids to police forces, fire departments, research, industry, and transport services. Radio spans continents in fractions of a second. Radio guides ships and aircraft with speed and safety through impenetrable fog, and issues warnings against icebergs, sandbanks, and mountains. Radio enables us to explore the earth for ores, water, coal, and oil. Radio provides information about the nature of the upper layers of the atmosphere, about the composition of the soil and the sea bed, and about worlds and galaxies far beyond the reach of our lives. Radio waves have also become a valuable tool for medicine; no hospital lacks equipment for radio-wave treatment today.

But there is no end in sight yet for the development of these waves.

Pioneers

The foundation for the discovery of radio waves was laid as early as 1831 in a series of experiments by Michael Faraday (1791–1867). This Englishman found that electrical energy can be transmitted to uncharged conductors even if no metallic contact takes place. Faraday concluded from this that a means of connecting the exciting body with the excited object must exist, as there is no such thing as an *"actio distans"* without a transmission medium. In his work on electromagnetic induction Faraday proved that magnetism and electricity are not two distinct forces, as had earlier been assumed; where time-varying electrical forces are in operation a magnetic field is formed, and where a time-varying magnetic field exists electrical forces are in action. He thus realized that the two were interdependent.

Faraday, the son of poor parents, had originally been apprenticed to a bookbinder. He applied for a position with Humphry (later Sir Humphry) Davy, the renowned chemist at the Royal Institution in London. Soon Faraday was taking part in the experiments at the latter's laboratory. In 1813 he became Sir Humphry's assistant, and twenty years later was made professor of chemistry at the Royal Institution. There he discovered the phenomenon of electromagnetic induction and formulated the law of chemical equivalents. In addition, he carried out research into the effect of magnetic fields on light, the diamagnetism of gases, and the magnetism of the earth, as well as discovering benzene. His work on the transmission of electricity without conducting wires became the starting point of an unending chain of inventions, all of them based on the principle of induction.

James Clerk Maxwell carried research into electromagnetic phenomena a good deal further and—theoretically, at any rate—opened the gate to the world of electromagnetic oscillations. He based his initial work on Faraday's conviction that an electric current or magnet could never excite another current or magnetic force at a distance if there were no medium of propagation between them. Faraday had not put his discoveries in mathematical formulas, and this was the task Maxwell set himself.

James Clerk Maxwell was born in Edinburgh in 1831, the year in which Faraday discovered the induction principle. His mathematical gifts became apparent even at the academy he attended in his home town as a boy; a paper, written when he was only fifteen, on a mechanical method of tracing Cartesian ovals was of such excellence that his teacher submitted it to the Royal Society of Edinburgh. At the age of twenty-five Maxwell, who had received his higher education at Cambridge, obtained the professorship of natural philosophy at Marischal College in Aberdeen, and at twenty-nine the chair of physics and astronomy at King's College, London. In 1868 he retired to his country place, Glenlair, Kirkcudbrightshire—only to be called from his seclusion two years later to become the first holder of the professorship of experimental physics in Cambridge. The plans for the Cavendish Laboratory were prepared under his supervision. His great treatise, *Electricity and Magnetism*, one of the most splendid accomplishments of the genius of a single man, appeared in 1873. In 1865 he had published his *Dynamical Theory of the Electromagnetic Field*.

The famous Maxwell equations giving the quantitative relationships between the dimensions of an electromagnetic field not only made possible an interpretation of induction but also linked the phenomena of optics to the field of electromagnetism.

Where Faraday had cautiously indicated that light stands in a close relationship to electricity, Maxwell stated that light is a special case of electromagnetic oscillation, and offered proof. He pointed out that if a magnet is moved not in the presence of a conductor of current but in the vicinity of a non-conductor such as glass or ebonite, it causes in the latter an electrical displacement that varies with the movement of the magnet. The displacement current does not appear immediately in the whole space, but is propagated at the speed of light.

Maxwell's equations show his certainty that there are electromagnetic waves and oscillations akin to those which produce visible light. He thus sensed the existence of radio waves two decades before they were discovered.

Hughes Experiments Unawares with Radio Waves

When the English-born American inventor David Edward Hughes—a man who had in the early 1850's begun experiments with a printing telegraph (a forerunner of today's teletype machine)—was in 1878 working on a machine that later became known as the microphone, he came very close to discovering electric waves. He found that whenever the strongly alternating current flowing through an arrangement of solenoids was interrupted, it produced an electric field of such strength that its presence could be demonstrated all over a room and even in several adjacent rooms. As control instruments Hughes made use of microphone contacts, ordinary carbon rods loosely held by two other pieces of carbon and linked up with a telephone. This led him to a search for a suitable form of receiver for electromagnetic waves, which, he said, obviously travel great distances, undeterred by walls and other obstacles in their path.

Receivers made of hard carbon and coke, when brought into contact with well-polished metal surfaces, proved to be extremely susceptible to the incoming currents, for they caused a deflection of a sensitive galvanometer. After the incidence of the electromagnetic waves, the galvanometer and the whole receiver automatically reverted to their original state.

These experiments were carried out nine years before Heinrich Hertz discovered radio waves. How close Hughes was to making this discovery is clear from the fact that at certain points in the room he noted a larger deflection of the galvanometer needle and stronger reception in the telephone. Knowing nothing of the character of the waves, he could offer no explanation of this phenomenon. He was dealing, to use Hertz's later terminology, with so-called *wave peaks* and *wave nodes* of the kind that always occur with *standing waves*.

Wireless systems were continually being tried out in the United States, although radio waves had not yet been discovered. In 1880 John Trowbridge succeeded in transmitting signals without wires. He set up a cable connection between the Harvard Observatory and Boston, and passed a strong current through it, interrupting it at regular intervals. The induction pulses so occasioned were picked up in a second cable about a mile away from the first. At about the same time another American, Amos E. Dolbear, applied for a patent on a system for wireless telegraphy through the earth. About twenty years before him Mahlon Loomis, a dentist in Philadelphia, had bridged a distance of fifteen miles by means of an oscillator of his own construction. He identified the signals intercepted by the deflections on a galvanometer. Loomis spoke of induced electrical

power. In 1873 he incorporated the Loomis Aerial Telegraph Company, but could not raise funds to pursue his
experiments further. An embittered man, he died in poverty.

"Lectures are Temporarily Suspended"

One November morning in 1886 the physics students at
the Karlsruhe Polytechnic found the door of the lecture
hall locked. "Lectures are temporarily suspended," a note
attached to the door read; "they will be resumed in two
weeks' time. (Signed) H. Hertz." As soon became known,
the professor had shut himself up in his laboratory, and
was said to spend even the nights there.

Heinrich Rudolf Hertz was born in 1857 in Hamburg,
the son of a well-to-do Jewish lawyer and senator of the
Free City. On leaving school, he began to study engineering, but abandoned it for the pursuit of physics. In Berlin
he studied under the great Heinrich von Helmholtz, and in
1883 qualified as a university lecturer at Kiel. Less than two
years later the twenty-eight-year-old Heinrich Hertz was
appointed professor at Karlsruhe.

Following Helmholtz's suggestion, the young scientist
had set himself the task of confirming Maxwell's mathe-
matically based theory that light is an electromagnetic
phenomenon and that waves considerably longer than light
waves must exist. It was in order to work undisturbed that
Hertz shut himself up in his laboratory for fourteen days.
The machinery Hertz used to excite these waves consisted
of an induction apparatus, a spark gap, and a galvanic battery; the receiver was a piece of wire shaped into a rectangle
or circle and fitted with a small adjustable spark gap. These
crude pieces of equipment were to be the first transmitter
and the first receiver in the world.

After some weeks of experiment the transmitter excited
waves six meters long and the receiver picked them up. As

soon as the transmitter was started up in the darkened room, a magnifying glass held at the spark gap in the wire ring showed tiny sparks flashing across. They were the sole proof of the existence of electromagnetic forces in the room.

Heinrich Hertz did not live to see the triumph of the waves he had discovered. He died, only thirty-seven years old, in Bonn, where he had become a full professor five years earlier.

Radio waves, then, were a reality. They could be produced without the slightest difficulty. All that was needed to propagate them was a small series of sparks, touched off by breaking a current. But all the men competent to judge, including Hertz, were convinced that without wires the waves could travel only a few yards. To make them cross a room of any size appeared quite impossible. The idea of transmitting them across the globe seemed nothing short of a dream, for the radio waves, it was thought, would never follow the curvature of the earth, but would get lost in space. Besides, how was one to find a method of receiving radio signals, the dots and dashes of the Morse alphabet, over a distance of yards? Hertz's receiving system, with his magnifying glass for watching sparks, provided for optical, not electrical, reception.

There was a device, invented by the Frenchman Edouard Branly in 1890 and named *coherer* by Oliver (afterward Sir Oliver) Lodge in 1894, which consisted of a small glass tube containing iron filings. But this primitive "receiving tube," which was neither exhausted of air nor had any other special features, was not in itself capable of receiving radio waves; it required an electric circuit, a battery, and a galvanometer—i.e., a sensitive measuring instrument. If a coherer was placed in the circuit, the iron filings became "fritted"—that is, they cohered or stuck together as soon as radio signals set up a current in the receiving circuit. This cohering process, which could not, of course, be

observed with the naked eye, altered the electrical resistance in the apparatus, and this change of resistance could
be read on the galvanometer. Confirmation that radio waves
had arrived was given by a deflection, sometimes only a
slight quiver, of the needle. After every signal the tube had
to be tapped with a little hammer to loosen the iron filings
again. Only then was the apparatus "clear" for the next
signal.

But people wanted to hear, not just see. To make this
possible, the galvanometer was exchanged for a sort of
headphone in which a slight crackle could be heard, but no
more. The coherer now consisted of a glass tube in which
two silver electrodes were set face to face one fiftieth of an
inch apart, with a mixture of nickel and silver filings occupying the intervening space. With this system the presence of radio waves could be registered a quarter of a mile
away.

The System Works!

To waves that cover 186,000 miles per second, a quarter
of a mile is of course next to nothing. Why was it that radio
systems quite powerful in themselves could not span a
greater distance? Aleksandr Stepanovich Popov (1859–
1905), a Russian physicist at the Electro-Technical Institute
of St. Petersburg, answered that question and came close to
inventing the wireless telegraph.

Working in the mid-1890's on the observation of approaching thunderstorms, he "trapped" the atmospheric
electricity in a vertical wire fastened to a kite in the air,
much as Benjamin Franklin had. With this arrangement
Popov hoped to receive electric waves at greater distances
than had been possible up to then. He did succeed in receiving some signals over a distance of thirty yards. What
Popov, however, failed to realize was that, in order to receive signals regularly, the transmitter—or sender, as tele-

graphers called it then—must be equipped with an antenna too.

This fact was later pointed out by Guglielmo Marconi, the younger son of an Italian businessman and his Irish-Scots wife. Born in 1874 in Bologna, Guglielmo had been educated privately. Very early he had taken a keen interest in physical and electrical science, and by the time he was twenty the idea that a system of telegraphy through space could be arrived at by means of Hertzian waves had firmly taken root in his mind. The summer of 1894 found him at his father's country place at Pontecchio, near Bologna. With his brother, Alfonso, he had set up a workshop in the villa; and the experiments carried on there impressed their father enough to induce him to lend financial assistance. In the spring of 1895 the young man was ready to experiment with wireless in the open.

He had constructed an oscillator, an instrument for producing vibration, similar to a machine built by Augustus Righi, a physicist at the University of Bologna. The receiver that Marconi used was Lodge's—or, rather, Branly's —coherer; it even boasted the hammer invented by the German J. P. Wagner (still in use today in electric bells), which Marconi employed to loosen the frittered metal filings in the coherer.

"The improvements that I made," Marconi recalled later, "were to connect both receiver and sender with first the earth and second the vertical wire insulated from the earth. The latter was by all means the more important of the two innovations." Or, to put it in the words of an Italian scientist: "The old Hertz radiator and old Branly coherer might be likened to the reed of an organ; by Marconi's improvements the pipe of the organ was added."

As the young experimenter could not at the same time watch both the transmitting and the receiving stations in his open-air tests, he posted his brother by the receiver— about 350 yards away—and armed him with a shotgun; as soon as there was a sound from the receiver, Alfonso was to fire a shot. And sure enough, it was not long before the crack of a gun rent the stillness of the countryside. Guglielmo Marconi's system worked!

He lost no time offering his invention to the Italian government. But it was suggested to him that perhaps he should go to England, as wireless was allied to the sea and there was greater shipping activity in that country. Also, his mother had relatives there, and so to England Marconi went.

Sir William Preece, Engineer-in-Chief of the British Post Office, at once recognized the importance of Marconi's system to an island cut off from the European mainland. True, there were undersea cables between the Continent and Britain. But what would happen if these cables were to be destroyed in time of war?

In Sir William, Marconi found a friend and supporter. He took out patents, one of them bearing the number 7777 that was long known in professional circles as the "four sevens patent." It was to become the cause of numerous disputes.

In the middle of May 1897 wire cables informed all the civilized countries that Guglielmo Marconi, a twenty-three-year-old Italian, had succeeded in transmitting a wireless signal by means of Hertzian waves over a three-mile stretch of British soil. Adolf Slaby of Berlin, who with Count Georg Arco witnessed the experiment, writes in his memoirs: "It will remain for me an unforgettable memory how, huddled together in a large wooden case on account of the strong wind, our eyes and ears concentrating intently on the receiving apparatus, we saw the flag hoisted as the prearranged signal, and suddenly heard the first clicking noise, the first clear Morse signals, being borne across to us silently and invisibly through the ether, that unknown, mysterious medium that forms our only bridge to the planets of the universe. It was the Morse signal for the letter 'V.' "

At first three miles, then five, and at the next attempt no less than nine miles were spanned by wireless signal. Soon the Marconi system was successfully covering distances of 100 and then up to 200 miles.

Events now crowded upon one another in rapid succession. In July 1897 the Wireless Telegraph and Signal Company Ltd. was formed in England to manufacture wireless equipment for lightships and lighthouses along the British coast. The firm, whose name was changed in 1900 to Marconi's Wireless Telegraph Co., Ltd., acquired Marconi's patents in all countries except one: loyal to his native country despite its initial indifference to his efforts, Marconi wanted Italy to be independent in case of war.

On June 3, 1898, the physicist Lord Kelvin sent the first paid wireless telegram. On March 3, 1899, for the first time, a telegraph on the coast chattered out an SOS signal sent by a ship in distress at sea. And a year later the first radio technicians in the world were working on a long-distance station that was to span the Atlantic Ocean; on both sides of the ocean, at Poldhu in Cornwall and at South Wellfleet on Cape Cod, a forest of antenna masts was springing up.

For this experiment Marconi needed electrical condensers big enough to be charged with adequate quantities of electricity. The only types known at that time were small glass bottles covered inside and out with thin wafers of tin foil; but these proved to be inadequate for the experiments. Marconi made some "bottles" of strong metal plates, using a layer of air between them as an insulator. Because of their size, he had to put up a special building for them. That is how, later, the "condenser house" at Clifden, Ireland, came to be constructed.

In view of the energies that had to be envisioned for spanning the Atlantic—the transmitter was to operate on twenty-five kilowatts, an unheard-of amount of power at that time—care had to be taken that the ball-shaped spark gaps, brass balls as big as a fist, were not fused into a lump by the enormous light arc. Here, too, Marconi found an excellent solution: he extinguished the light arc created by each flashover by means of a special device that, in the conditions then prevailing, was a stroke of genius.

The preliminary work for the project lasted almost a year. On the shores of the Atlantic in Cornwall stood a handful of rough-and-ready wooden huts housing the equipment on which the ears of the entire world were trained: beside the twenty antenna masts rising to a height of about 200 feet they were dwarfed into insignificance. The inventor maintained contact by cable with his collaborators over on the North American coast. It was agreed that the first signal should be three dots, the letter "S" in the Morse code. However, on September 17, 1901, a heavy storm on the English side blew down the masts and destroyed the conical antenna. A few weeks later a similar fate overtook the masts at Cape Cod. To save time, the antenna in England was not re-erected in its original form, but was spread fanwise between two 150-foot masts. Early in November 1901 the preparations were at last completed, and Marconi now decided to carry out the first test in Newfoundland, the nearest point in North America to Europe.

On November 26, 1901, he left England with George S. Kemp and P. W. Paget and arrived in Newfoundland on December 6. After inspecting a number of sites, he found what he considered the best one on Signal Hill, overlooking the port. There, in the old military barracks then used as a hospital, he and his collaborators set up their apparatus. A 600-foot length of wire, envisioned as their antenna, was to be held up by a free balloon. But a squall carried away the balloon. At last, on December 12, a kite kept the antenna in the air for a few hours, and at 12.30 p.m. Marconi handed his earphones to Kemp, who stood waiting at his side. Through the deafening crackle and clatter of the atmospheric discharges Kemp heard the prearranged signal repeated again and again—the three "dots" of the Morse letter "S."

The world received the epoch-making news with amazement. When the first newspaper story was radioed across the Atlantic about two years later, the astonishment had already somewhat ebbed, because there probably has never been another field in which invention has followed so hard upon invention, in which one design has so swiftly been depreciated by another, as in the area of wireless communication.

"The bewildering possibility of telegraphy without wires," as Sir William Crookes had called it, writing with remarkable vision in 1892, had become a reality on that December day in 1901. Now the King of Italy conferred a knighthood upon the young wizard, and soon universities vied with one another in bestowing honorary degrees upon him. In 1909 he shared the Nobel Prize for physics with Karl Ferdinand Braun.

Marconi intervened again and again in the development of the young techniques of telegraphy and enriched them with a series of important inventions. Only the most significant need be mentioned: the timed spark system; the coupled, tuned transmitting and receiving antenna; the rotary spark gap; and the horizontal directional antenna, a forerunner of the radar antenna.

In 1927, Marconi, now a Marchese, lost one eye in a motor accident. He relinquished the presidency of the Marconi Company and retired to his yacht, *Elettra*, which henceforth served him as both a home and a laboratory.

In 1937, while the primitive apparatus he had used in his first long-range tests was being shown at the Paris World Exposition, he succumbed to a heart attack at the age of sixty-three. Transmitting stations throughout the world were silenced upon the receipt of the news, and the flags on their buildings were lowered to half-mast.

Modest Beginnings

Adolf Slaby (1849–1913), who had attended Marconi's experiments in England, returned to Berlin and set up a laboratory in the Charlottenburg district. Experimenting with radio waves, he soon managed to establish wireless contact between his laboratory and a nearby building. He then built a transmitting station in the Imperial Gardens, with the receiving station—its antenna attached to a tall mast—situated at a distance of about two miles. In October 1897 Slaby continued his tests at the Schöneberg firing range, using a transmitting station thirteen miles away. There for the first time captive instead of free balloons were employed to carry the antenna. This arrangement prevented the antennas, often 600 to 1,000 feet tall, from being carried away by the wind.

Reception was excellent in good weather. But in stormy weather, atmospheric discharges caused heavy static; at intervals the aerial conductors set off such violent discharges that the men working the apparatus were sometimes in serious danger.

At the time Slaby started his experiments in and near Berlin, Karl Ferdinand Braun was working in the same field, in Strasbourg. Braun had constructed the closed oscillator circuit, a device that made it possible to work with particular wave lengths and to single out individual transmitters more easily. By means of a flywheel switchgear Braun also made the antenna less susceptible to atmospheric disturbances. Finally, he improved grounding by the use of a wire net stretched out on the ground as an electric counterweight.

The establishment of the Prof. Braun's Telegrafie G.m.b.H.[1] marked the start of a veritable race between this group, which used the Braun-Arco system, and the British Marconi Company operating the Marconi system. The battle was waged with all the resources at the disposal of the participants; in practice they both had to work with the same basic methods.

In the early days transmission generally was carried out by the *explosive-spark system,* so named because when the flashovers occurred between the points of a spark gap, they sounded like the rattle of machine-gun fire. With Braun's arrangement it was possible to count on a maximum of 100 sparks in succession per second. This meant as many as 100 sparks flashing across a single spark gap every second, and for those who had to monitor these radio signals it was anything but pleasant. Max Wien of Jena thought of a remedy: he divided the spark gap into several smaller ones; now the sparks could be *quenched* more rapidly, and the number of sparks in a row could be raised to 1,000 per second. This faster flow of sparks produced a much more clear-cut note that could be heard unmistakably above all the crackle of atmospheric distortion. Among professionals this process rapidly became known as the *quenched-spark system.*

The explosive-spark and quenched-spark systems were the two original transmitting procedures. The *electric-arc system* was added to them within a few short years.

In 1903 Valdemar Poulsen, a Dane, constructed an electric-arc transmitter with which continuous *undamped* oscillations could be produced. This invention and the "singing arc" devised by the Englishman William du Bois Duddell aroused enormous interest; it was hoped that these improvements would pave the way to wireless telephony—up to then merely transmission of Morse signals had been possible. However, results were modest at the beginning.

. . .

[1] See p. 129.

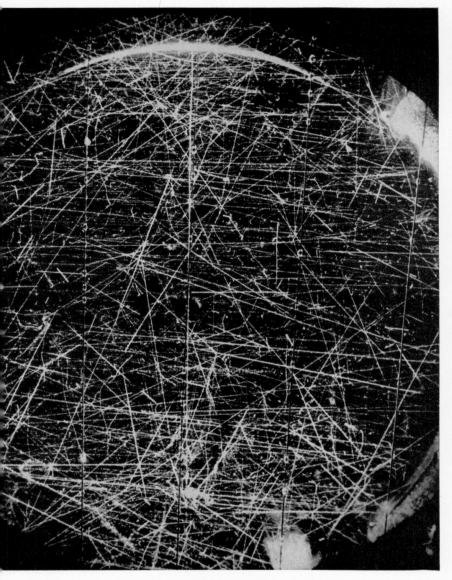

Billion-volt atomic particles in the Brookhaven cosmotron
—one of the first cloud-chamber photographs obtained
with the cosmotron in operation. [*courtesy:* BROOKHAVEN
NATIONAL LABORATORY]

Decca Marine Radar on a small vessel. [*courtesy:* DECCA RADAR (CANADA), L

Offshore radar station, 100 miles east of Cape Cod, Massachusetts.
[*photograph:* Philip Gendreau]

Indicator unit showing controls and signals on a cathode-ray tube. From these "blips"—signals sent out by home-based ground stations—the operator can calculate his position, perhaps hundreds of miles from home, and, by means of a special map, obtain a fix accurate to within a few miles. [BRITISH OFFICIAL PHOTOGRAPH]

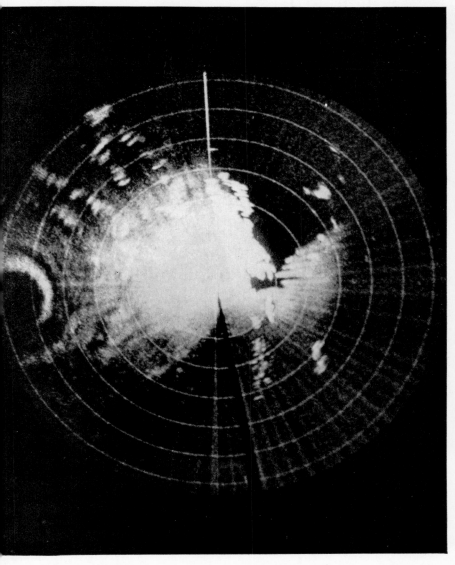

Radar scope showing a hurricane. [*photograph:* Philip Gendreau]

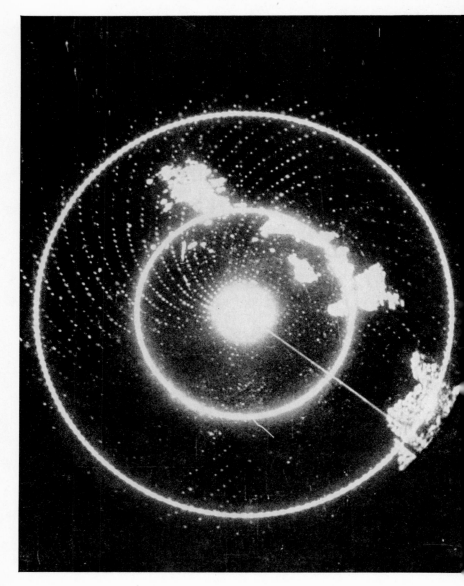

The Hawaiian Islands from an altitude of 10,000 feet—a
welcome sight for air-borne early-warning flight crews of
the Pacific Barrier Command. When this scene appears on
their radar scopes, their patrol is almost completed.
[Official U.S. Navy Photograph]

ntenna used in a radar moon experiment. [*photograph:* Philip
ᴇɴᴅʀᴇᴀᴜ]

U.S. NAVY
COMMUNICATION MOON RELAY SYSTEM

e moon relays Navy
ssages between Ha-
i and Washington.
ꜰꜰɪᴄɪᴀʟ U.S. Nᴀᴠʏ
ᴜꜱᴛʀᴀᴛɪᴏɴ]

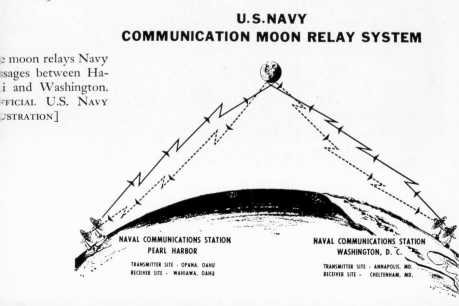

**NAVAL COMMUNICATIONS STATION
PEARL HARBOR**

TRANSMITTER SITE - OPANA, OAHU
RECEIVER SITE - WAHIAWA, OAHU

**NAVAL COMMUNICATIONS STATION
WASHINGTON, D. C.**

TRANSMITTER SITE - ANNAPOLIS, MD.
RECEIVER SITE - CHELTENHAM, MD.

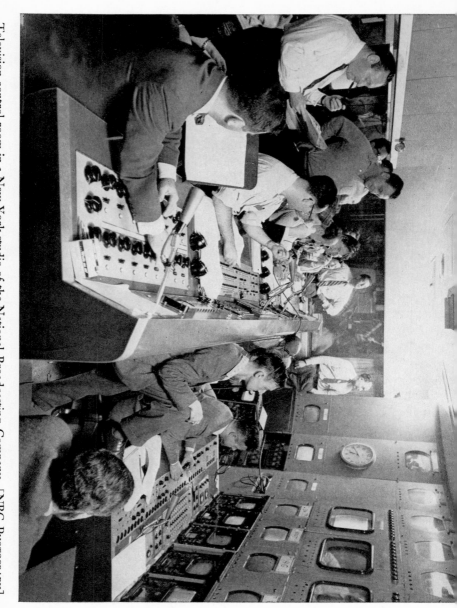

Television control room in a New York studio of the National Broadcasting Company. [NBC Photograph]

When the first United States army units set foot on German soil in the spring of 1945, they carried a radio apparatus that people at once dubbed *"Masskrug"* (tankard); in fact, the famous walkie-talkie was not much bigger than a beer tankard of the type used at the Munich Hofbräuhaus. To the surprise of the Germans, the GI's using the Masskrug could talk freely to each other over a distance of several miles. Wiring parts, tubes, batteries, and antenna were deftly housed in a sort of telephone receiver. Perhaps some of the older men in conquered Germany, watching the performance of the walkie-talkie, could not help casting their minds back to the first military wireless telegraphs they themselves had seen or heard about.

In 1902 the entire equipment of the "wireless corps" of the German army consisted of three mobile stations and one fixed station. When one of the mobile stations was to be readied for operation, the rear section of the vehicle, which contained the transmitter, was limbered up to the front section, which held the receiver. The station further housed a gas engine, a dynamo, an inductor, the spark gap, a transformer, and the transmitting key weighing about six pounds. The antenna used was a thin, flexible steel cable some 600 feet long; when there was plenty of wind, the cable was carried aloft by a folding kite, and if the wind was light, by a balloon. To ensure that the balloon could be filled with hydrogen gas at any time, the crew always had five cylinders of the gas with them, enough to fill two balloons. The personnel of this "corps" consisted of four commissioned officers, five non-coms, and eighteen enlisted men. Of the latter, six were signal-corps men by training, three were railroadmen, and nine were airship specialists. The signal-corps men (telgraphers) and the non-coms sat at the receiving sets; the railroadmen, trained "mechanics," watched and regulated the motor in the transmitter; the airship specialists looked after kites and balloons. These mobile stations were moved by teams of six horses.

What higher-ups in the Germany army thought about radiotelegraphy at that time is shown by the words of General (afterward Field Marshal) Count Haeseler. "Captain," he is quoted as having said to one of the officers at a radio station, "if I wanted to be sure of having a message delivered, I for one should prefer dispatching a couple of mounted orderlies."

The German navy was somewhat more venturesome. Braun's assistant, Jonathan Zenneck, was called in for long-range tests between Cuxhaven and the lightship *Elbe* in 1902. In the course of his work Zenneck worked out a method of determining direction by means of radio waves. Soon reception of radio signals up to a distance of seventy miles was perfect.

In 1904 radio sets manufactured by the Telefunkengesellschaft für drahtlose Telegrafie, a German company established the year before, received their baptism of fire in the Russo-Japanese War. They were effective up to distances of about 125 miles.

As early as 1901 the portable radio sets contained rotary condensers for tuning purposes; this type of condenser consisted of a *rotor* section and a *stator* section, blocks of metal plates which could be rotated in and out of each other without their having contact. Employed to tune transmitter and receiver to each other, this condenser weighed quite a few pounds; it operated in a container of oil to prevent sparks from flashing between the rotor plates and the stator plates. Electrolytic cells or detectors were used in general for the radio waves; they were all non-adjustable, and were housed in a special casing. The form favored in those days for transmitting coils was the pyramid winding, based on a procedure in which the wire is wound on the frame of the coil in the shape of a pyramid.

At about that same time a machine that supplied high-frequency current was already under construction. It became the basis of the high-frequency generator, which for years to come formed the heart of every transmitter. Later, quietly and without fanfare, a rival to the high-frequency generator was developed—the transmitting tube.

A Steady Flow of Improvements

Inventions came hot and hard on one another's heels in those days just before World War I. The rotary condenser was improved by milling the plates out of a metal block, or simply by making the whole plate complex in the form of a casting. N. Kramolin, a German engineer, constructed a rotary condenser with slotted plates to ensure better tracking in multi-stage receivers.

In 1912 the American E. H. Armstrong invented the regenerative coil, also known as the feedback, and was issued a patent in October 1914. This invention, which became the basis of the tube transmitter, is sometimes credited also to the Austrian Alexander Meissner, who worked independently of Armstrong and achieved results at about the same time.

In Germany efforts to build up an overseas radio network began as early as 1906. At the same time the first passenger ships were equipped with radio. Nauen, a town twenty-two miles northwest of Berlin, was chosen as the place for the first—and for some years only—high-power station; when its power had been raised to thirty kilowatts in 1909, it became possible to increase the operational range of the transmitter to 3,000 miles.

After a radio installed in a British dirigible in 1910 had been able to pick up Morse signals sent by a ground station, the first German radio battalion was set the task of establishing contact with a transmitter in a zeppelin. However, some of the military men were afraid that the radio signals intercepted by the receiving apparatus in the gondola might cause the highly inflammable hydrogen gas to explode. Although physicists had dismissed that fear, a great many of the army men present when the tests started gazed anxiously up at the zeppelin floating some 3,000 feet high, expecting it to blow up at any moment. But nothing untoward happened, and clear communication was achieved between the ground station and the airship.

Meantime, trials with radio apparatus on railway trains had been started in the United States. In 1912 the first practical results were achieved on a train of the Delaware, Lackawanna and Western Railroad.

The enormous importance of radio telegraphy to shipping became manifest to the world with the disaster of the *Titanic* on April 15, 1912. More than 700 passengers on that ship, which ran into an iceberg on her maiden voyage, owed their lives to the unceasing SOS calls of her radio officer.

In that year the third International Radio Conference was held in London. The display of progress included the showing of a low-frequency amplifier equipped with tubes, an invention of the Austrian Robert von Lieben. This type of amplifier was, however, capable only of amplifying signals at sound frequencies that came from a microphone.

At the outbreak of World War I the German armed forces were equipped with portable and fitted radiotelegraphy sets. Soon a special type for trench warfare was developed, but the range was still very limited. To boost efficiency—in particular, of monitoring sets—use was made of "superhets," receivers with a special circuit, the *superheterodyne circuit*, which was responsive to even the feeblest energies received. The invention of the capacitive-resistance coupling by the American B. J. Arnold made it possible to build effective amplifiers at low cost.

When the trans-Atlantic cable was severed by the British shortly after the outbreak of the war, the Nauen station proved able to assume the entire burden of telegraphic communication between Germany and the American continent. Not only had the output power of Nauen been increased repeatedly in 1912–13, but its antenna had been raised to a height of 850 feet. But Marconi lodged a protest, requesting that the station at Sayville, New York, be closed. He also sued the two German companies for patent infringement.

Meantime, the first high-power radio station for the United States Navy had been designed and installed by Lee de Forest, an American who is sometimes called "the father of radio." Born in 1873 in Council Bluffs, Iowa, he had ever since the turn of the century devoted his energies to the development of wireless telegraphy and radiotelephony. He was the first to use the alternating-current generator and transmitter. Perhaps the most important of his inventions was the electron tube (vacuum tube), which presented the young science of radio engineering with the means of constructing better and smaller transmitters and receivers. Above all, it enabled the industry to work out superheterodyne circuits that operated not with explosive spark gaps or high-frequency generators, as had been the case previously, but with simple tubes. This brought about the birth of the tube transmitter and with it the birth of *radio telephony*.

In 1916 the first radio news went over the air in the United States. In the same year the first radio station was established.

From the outset of the war, efforts were made in both camps to find ways and means of locating and "monitoring" enemy stations. A procedure of this nature, in which loop direction finders or even simple loop antennas were used, was outlined by the Italian Alessandro Artom, who had discovered that loop antennas exhibited directional properties. By this we mean the property of a loop antenna which enables it to improve reception in a receiver when the frame is turned in the direction of the transmitter. If it is turned away from that direction, reception becomes weaker. However, the position of the transmitter cannot be pinpointed by means of a single loop antenna; a second one must be set up at some distance. This second antenna is likewise turned until the reception strength is at peak. If the position of the two loop antennas is now marked on an accurate map and the exact angle between them is measured, two lines can be drawn whose intersection shows the location of the transmitter.

If the transmitter is moved, its position has to be located afresh. If the intersection is found to lie on a body of water —for example, at sea—this proves that a ship's transmitter is involved. At the instance of the British Admiralty, Marconi began working on an improvement of Artom's method and succeeded so well that the navy was able to "watch" the German high-seas fleet emerge from Wilhelmshaven one day late in May 1916 and to follow its course; with this information in hand, the Admiralty ordered interception of the enemy fleet off Jutland. For the first time in history radio location procedure had tracked down enemy craft; the method had established not only their direction but also the approximate number of ships.

The German efforts to mass-produce radio sets for the armed forces had, at about the same time, led Heinrich Barkhausen to construct a special kind of tube, the so-called *tetrode*, a tube containing four elements, a plate, and two grids. It could be used with many types of circuit, and had the particular advantage of functioning with substantially lower anode voltages than usual. For this reason preference was given to the tetrode wherever, as in the case of portable receivers, it was important to economize on anode batteries. Simultaneously with this tube a mass-produced transmitter made its appearance and diverted attention from all other transmission systems. With this development the vacuum-tube transmitter began its great advance.

On July 28, 1915, the American Telephone and Telegraph Company, working together with the Western Electric Company, succeeded in telephoning by radio from Arlington, Virginia, to Hawaii—a distance of close to 5,000 miles; some months later the Arlington station could establish communication, across the Atlantic, with the Eiffel Tower in Paris.

Shortly after the end of World War I attention began to be focused, both in the United States and in Britain, upon the enormous value of radio for aviation. In 1923 the American Louis Alton Hazeltine was granted a patent for the non-radiating neutrodyne receiver.

Around 1928 radio telegraphy was in use in all civilized countries of the world.

The "Century of Wireless"

Amateur radio operators had been numerous even before the war in some countries. From 1919 on they began to work in telephony rather than Morse telegraphy. In England broadcasting started quite spontaneously with amateur performances, transmissions of records, etc.

Soon the radio industry everywhere undertook experimental work on the improvement of microphones and the construction of listening apparatus that could be operated with little technical knowledge. Arrangements for regular transmissions of programs, frequently involving legal problems, were made in the Western countries even before the conditions for broadcasting were explored satisfactorily. It was understood readily that an innovation whose historical importance was second only to the invention of the printing press had made its appearance.

In Germany a similar development was due to the efforts of one man. Hans Bredow, a high official in the Ministry of Posts, had been interested in radio engineering even as a high-school student. As a front-line soldier he had now and then transmitted some mouth-organ music right in the trenches, much to the amusement of the Allied monitors. After the war he had been given the job of putting the Nauen station back into operation. But his attempts to initiate broadcasting for information and entertainment met with a total lack of understanding. Hans Dominik, an early science-fiction writer, commented on one of Bredow's lectures, in the highly respected *Berliner Lokalanzeiger*, as follows: "While the speaker kept his feet on the ground, he nevertheless expounded from time to time ideas daring enough to do credit to Jules Verne. An example of this was his description of an orator of the future delivering a speech into an apparatus without wires, and yet making his words audible to millions of people. . . ." A year later a radio station operated by the postal service broadcast an orchestral concert. But the official inauguration of German broadcasting was delayed until the end of 1923.

Today a network of thousands of radio stations spans the globe. A huge industry concentrates on the production of tubes, resistors, condensers, loudspeakers, microphones, measuring instruments, etc., and, of course, on the assembly of complete sets. It is worth recalling once in a while that all of this grew out of a spark coil, a battery, and an ordinary hoop of wire—grew, to put it accurately, out of an idea and the persistence and endurance of a handful of men, by no means all "professionals."

In these days we not only find radios and small transmitters operated by solar energy, but amplifiers are made which take up no more room than an ordinary matchbox. This process of miniaturization recently achieved a triumph with the introduction of hearing aids in which the whole amplifying system and the sources of power are housed in the framework of a pair of spectacles. The kernel of these tiny apparatuses is a capsule the size of a pea which takes the place of the usual rectifying and amplifying tube. This miniature tube consists of little more than a core of germanium, either crystalline in structure or "grown," and a few tiny hair wires. There is no longer a hot filament supplying electrons, as in the case of the radio tube. These tiny tubes, known as *transistors,* cannot burn out. They likewise need no heater current and no transformer of their own to supply the necessary heater voltage. In battery sets the heating battery is rendered superfluous.

In principle, the classic radio tube is essentially a special kind of incandescent lamp, and the first tube constructors stuck to this prototype absolutely. They took an evacuated glass flask with a heater filament and installed facing it a simple metal plate to act as an anode. If positive potential was applied to this plate, the arrangement could be used to convert an alternating current into a direct current. Later a fine wire grating was inserted between the heating filament and the aforementioned plate. By this means the tube could be *modulated*—i.e., an audio current reaching the wire grating could be amplified. A tube of this kind could be used to perform two functions: it could rectify and it could amplify.

This was the beginning of the unparalleled development of the amplifier tube. It turned up throughout the electronics industry in hundreds of variants. Its effects were particularly fertile in communications techniques. Nevertheless, all these tubes still show certain deficiencies. They may burn out or break, and their efficiency declines after about 1,000 working hours. At times, too, their vacuum is destroyed by tiny hair cracks, and they become useless. They also tend to develop internal short circuits because these once primitive instruments have developed into uncommonly delicate technical marvels in which tolerances of

between one hundredth and one thousandth of a millimeter
are normal. For a long time these deficiencies were accepted
as inevitable. Then in 1945 a team of American physicists—
William Schockley, John Bardeen, and Walter Brattain—
discovered a peculiar property of the metal germanium.
It was found that germanium crystals to which a tiny
quantity of another metal had been added could be used as
both rectifiers and amplifiers. The device was called a
transistor. The significant thing is that the transistor requires much less energy to achieve the desired effects than a
tube.

The transistor is the baby of communications technology.
It represents probably the greatest advance in this field
since the invention of the radio tube. A miniature germanium plate one tenth of an inch wide and one twentieth of
an inch thick can perform many of the functions of a tube.
It has opened up altogether new possibilities for radio and
television. Radio and television sets have been fitted with
transistors in such a way that they contain no tubes except
the output tube and a picture tube. The television set in
question weighs no more than twenty-seven pounds. The
whole range of tubes required is replaced by thirty-seven
small transistors. Extremely light and simple transistor receivers have acquired importance in stage production. These
sets consist of nothing but a headset of modern design
weighing about two ounces, the hoop serving as the antenna.

Transistors are also being applied with great success in
modern computers, the electronic brains. A computer of
this kind normally requires a complement of some thousands of tubes, whose installation and wiring increase its
dimensions accordingly. With transistors, computers and
other "thinking" machines can now be built which combine
predictable performance with manageable size. One experimental model has been built in America which, with no loss
of efficiency, takes up only a tenth of the conventional

space and consumes only one sixtieth of the normal amount of power.

Telephone engineers have used transistors to construct a control mechanism for long-distance calls which, when a button is pressed, goes on dialing the code until the person at the other end answers. If the control mechanism does not get through at the first attempt, the dialed request is stored in a storage unit and waits for a while before automatically dialing again. Where we, in the case of a six-digit telephone number, need twelve to fourteen seconds to dial, this apparatus takes only a third of a second. The possibilities inherent in the use of transistors have already taken on fairly definite shape, so that the automation of industry now in process will enormously increase the demand for this cheap substitute for tubes.

Heating by Short Wave

In 1881—that is, even before the discovery of Hertzian waves—a New York neurologist, Dr. William James Morton, began to use, without being aware of the fact, electrical oscillatory energy in the treatment of patients. His ray-therapy apparatus consisted of a strong induction machine made up of two induction coils and an iron core. One of the coils carried many windings of thin wire, the other a few windings of thick wire. There was also a hammer that interrupted the current when the piece of iron on it was attracted by the iron core of the induction machine. The current interrupted by the hammer produced a make-and-break pulse in the thick-wire winding. That pulse could be so strong that if a spark gap were introduced, it could strike across the intervening air and produce sparks. Morton placed the part of the body to be treated in the circuit between two metal electrodes, a practice that is still followed today.

Around 1900 Nikola Tesla, an Austrian-born American (1857–1943), constructed a transformer that produced high-frequency currents of very high voltage and extremely low current. Besides being displayed as a curiosity, this transformer was widely used for medical purposes after it had been discovered that very high-frequency current of very high voltage was harmless to human beings, and in fact caused superficial warming of the skin. Still, the medical world on the whole held aloof from "such frivolities."

At about the same time the French physicist Jacques Arsène d'Arsonval became interested in the subject. In his studies of the effects of high-frequency current on the living organism he had noted the heat generated in the body, but he failed to realize that treatment with this heat was capable of producing good results. On the contrary, d'Arsonval regarded the heat as a most troublesome subsidiary phenomenon of his experiments.

R. von Zeynek was the first to appreciate the properties of this heat effect: it meant that diseased areas of the body, previously inaccessible or accessible only with difficulty to external thermal treatment, could be reached by generated *internal heat*.

In 1905 another German researcher, W. von Preyp, following this basic concept, began therapeutic experiments. The results encouraged his collaborator, A. von Bernd, to build the first medical high-frequency apparatus, which was successfully used mainly for treating joint ailments. But a large section of the medical profession raised a storm against such treatment, casting doubt on the healing effects of high-frequency current. Others talked of spurious successes, and still others tried to disparage the process by maintaining that very soon after an initial improvement the disorders recurred with greater severity than before. In spite of all this, the treatment, under the name *diathermy*, gradually gained a hold in medical circles; and today there is scarcely a hospital that does not make use of such appliances.

Essentially, the original types of diathermy apparatus consisted of a small quenched-spark transmitter supplying waves ranging from 300 to 600 meters in length. These were later replaced by the medium-wave tube transmitter until the discovery was finally made that shorter waves produce considerably greater heat with far less expenditure of power. Here, as so often in the annals of discovery, chance played a part.

The Chicken That Fell into a Coma

A general physician had his office out on the fringes of a large city near some transmitting masts. One day a man came to him complaining of chronic headaches. The patient was a technician at the nearby radio station. Soon afterward his assistant appeared, and a little later the chief engineer as well as four other technicians who complained as one man of headaches, great drowsiness, discomfort around the heart, shortness of breath, and shooting pains in the limbs. It was clear to the doctor that these symptoms very probably pointed to a single cause. His inquiries showed that these people all worked near the large oscillator of the new ultrashort-wave transmitter that had just started operating at the local station. Could it be that short waves were producing these phenomena?

Very shortly afterward, in the summer of 1929, quite a number of scientists on both sides of the Atlantic began to turn their attention to the problem of these rays and their peculiar effects. The experiments that were carried out yielded an extraordinary amount of information. For instance, a chicken was directly exposed to the rays of an ultrashort-wave transmitter, with the startling result that after first fluttering about in agitation, the bird suddenly became strikingly placid and then huddled in a heap on the ground. Even after the radiation was cut off, it was impossible to excite any kind of reaction in the chicken; it did not respond even to pinpricks. It had obviously suffered paralysis of the brain as a consequence of the radiation. It did not recover for several hours.

After the chicken was exposed to radiation for a longer period the next day, it did not regain its power of movement even after several hours. It had lapsed into a coma, and finally had to be killed because its brain was completely paralyzed. Was there a parallel to be drawn between the results of these experiments and the puzzling behavior of birds of passage? Had it not been observed often that as soon as such birds flew into the vicinity of a powerful transmitter, they were thrown into great confusion? Was it not well known that when this happened, they generally alighted somewhere and did not continue their flight until the transmitter had been switched off? During World War II the behavior of such birds was studied more closely with the aid of radar beams—i.e., tightly focused, very short-wave radio beams. If these were directed at a flock of ducks, they scattered almost instantaneously, acting as if they had been shot at. In certain cases they grew so bewildered that they darted off in all directions.

Equally interesting were the results of subjecting bacteria and small creatures to these rays. Cultures of bacilli and bacteria placed in the high-frequency field of an ultrashort-wave transmitter were severely damaged or utterly destroyed in a short time. Under a brief dose of radiation the tiny eggs of a great variety of insects—moths' eggs, for instance—burst and were killed. Meal worms at first swelled up inordinately and then shrank to the size of maggots before they perished, drying up completely. Mold on bread died after thirty seconds under radiation. Slices of bread, irradiated in their packaging for about a minute, were found to be in perfect condition even after three weeks of storage in unfavorable circumstances. With damp corn, only fifteen seconds of radiation on a five-meter wave length were needed not only to dry it but also to neutralize the dreaded grain weevil.

In regard to experiments on silkworms and their eggs during development, we have this report from Italian researchers: "If the radiation was administered in doses that could not have harmful results, it had the effect of markedly promoting growth. For these experiments, three-meter waves were the ones mainly used. The irradiated silkworms were about 100 per cent heavier than those not subjected to radiation. The entire yield was expanded by one tenth. During three years of experiment no diseases were observed in the otherwise extremely delicate silkworms. In general, irradiated worms began to spin six or seven days earlier, and the eggs were laid three or four days sooner than usual."

The influence of ultrashort waves on the germination, development, and life of plants was the subject of some highly interesting experiments. The wave length used was 1.5 meters and the transmitted power only 0.1 watt. It was shown that an increase in the rate of growth occurs in plants when the intensity of radiation is kept within small limits. If the dose is increased, the result is a distinct decline in growth. These experiments were prompted by observation of what are called ultrashort-wave tree lines—wooded areas in the neighborhood of short-wave transmitters which are manifestly backward in their growth. The experiments supplied confirmation of the view that ultrashort-wave radiation from the sun, particularly strong during periods of sunspot activity, also affects the growth of plants.

The property possessed by ultrashort waves of heating objects of all kinds from within has been applied to thawing out frozen ground—which it does very quickly. Ultrashort waves are also used, to an increasing extent, in the processing of non-conducting materials such as wood, paper, rubber, leather, and synthetic resin. For some time they have enabled timber specialists to glue plywood at an incredibly fast rate. For the plastics specialist they "weld" individual sheets in a matter of seconds, or warm various types of powdered plastics to make them easier to process. With ultrashort waves the chemist sterilizes his bandages through their packaging, and the miller sterilizes and dries his corn, flour, and semolina.

The idea of using high-frequency heat for steaming and roasting goes back twenty years. Nowadays the use of high-frequency grills has become part and parcel of a modern kitchen.

Factories using ultrashort waves, mainly for canning purposes, with a power of up to 300 watts exist today in the United States and in Russia. Where metals have to be heated, melted, or hardened, the apparatus used consists simply of a few metal windings or even a single wire loop through which a high-frequency current is passed. If the object under treatment is enclosed in a coil, the eddy currents generated cause strong superficial heat. This can be boosted to the point where the object becomes red hot and melts.

This process is widely used nowadays for heat treatment of gears, shafts, and the inside walls of borings. Its advantage lies in the fact that heat treatment is localized where it is required, and is completed very rapidly. In the case of gears, for instance, only the rubbing surfaces are treated. The hard layer that is formed goes no deeper than one thirtieth of an inch. In most items a layer of this sort is thoroughly adequate to withstand the many and varied forms of wear and tear.

CHAPTER 9

From the "Telemobiloscope" to Radar

HEINRICH HERTZ had shown as early as 1887 that radio waves behave like light rays; they can be focused, they are reflected by mirrors, ordinary metal surfaces, or wire gratings, and they can be picked up again as a rebounding radio echo. A year later Nikola Tesla, writing on these phenomena, suggested that the Hertzian waves' capacity to be reflected could be used to establish the position and the course of a moving object.

This paper may or may not have come to the attention of Christian Hülsmeyer, a Düsseldorf engineer to whom several countries granted patents in 1904 for a radio-echo collision-prevention device. The German patent attested that Hülsmeyer had invented a "process for reporting distant metallic objects to an observer by means of electric waves." His apparatus, the "Telemobiloscope," is described as a device "by means of which the approach or movement of distant metallic objects (trains, ships, or the like) is reported . . . by audible or visual signals." The invention, the patent points out, is "based upon the property possessed by electric waves of being reflected by metals; electric waves are used here to exert direct influence on a signal device."

Hülsmeyer demonstrated his invention to representatives of several large shipping companies he had invited to Rotterdam. But none of these showed any interest in the tests, which went off according to plan. Of course he also tried to interest the German Navy Office in his patent; but neither the German admirals nor their confreres in other countries were willing to take a closer look at the Telemobiloscope, let alone advance the funds necessary for development of the apparatus. Nor did the *Titanic* catastrophe alter this general indifference; it must, however, be added in fairness that it was not yet known that snow and ice also reflect radio waves.

Hülsmeyer allowed his patents to lapse, and his instruments became museum pieces. The Düsseldorf Museum can now boast of possessing the first "radar sets" in the world, bequeathed to the city by Herr Hülsmeyer himself.

Why the invention was not developed during World War I, why, indeed, no one appears to have remembered it, is incomprehensible. Only loop direction finders were used in that war; and while this method enabled the British to ascertain when the German warships sailed and to follow their course, the process worked only when the ships' radios were exchanging wireless messages. With the Hülsmeyer Telemobiloscope, somewhat improved, the ships could have been detected without radio traffic.

Nothing was heard of the process until after World War I. In 1922 Marchese Marconi, speaking in New York, said: "It seems to me that it should be possible to design apparatus by means of which a ship could radiate or project a divergent beam of rays . . . which, if coming across a metallic object, . . . would be reflected back to a receiver screened from the local transmitter on the sending ship, and thereby immediately reveal the presence and bearing of the other ship in fog or thick weather."

Successful radar systems were developed independently during the years 1934–40 in the United States, England, France, and Germany. In Germany the ultrashort-wave band was the pet field of a number of general-staff officers. Ultrashort waves interested them because they made possible *directional monitoring*. Monitoring of broadcasts was practically ruled out unless the position of the transmitter and its wave length were known. A disadvantage that had to be accepted was the fact that ultrashort waves are propagated only along the line of sight. If, for example, an obstacle such as a mountain stood between the transmitter and the receiver, reception was impossible. The roughness of the earth's surface thus precluded long-distance transmission from the start. On water the situation was very different. This was why the navy was the first of the German services to start genuinely serious experiments.

In March 1934 some noteworthy tests were begun in the Bay of Lübeck. The old battleship *Hessen* was swept with radio beams from a sixty-centimeter transmitter, and it was found that they were reflected by the ship's sides. Certainly the distance was short: barely twenty-two yards. But two months later the measured distance had already been lengthened to a mile and a quarter. Next the transmitter and the antenna system were improved. It had been realized that the radio beam must be very narrow and must not scatter unduly if distances of any size were to be achieved. This time the *Grille* functioned as the trial ship. Although Germany possessed an establishment for these and similar experiments at Pelzerhaken on the Baltic coast, Admiral Cailiax declared that "this radio business is not so urgent";

the navy was building motor torpedo boats. Faced with a shortage of funds, the researchers abandoned the short wave lengths and built radio ranging sets operating on waves of 1.5 and 2.4 meters. This was in January 1936, and the apparatus was envisioned for antiaircraft work. These were the first radar sets used by the Wehrmacht. During maneuvers near Swinemünde they detected aircraft at ranges of up to sixty miles.

The Luftwaffe thereupon decided to place an order for this equipment, which was given the name *Freya*. However, its further development was to prove impracticable. As the antenna system was too unwieldy for the fairly long wave length employed, the latter was again shortened, and sets were built to operate on a wave length of eighty centimeters. In 1938 this radar set was ready, and was installed in the battleship *Graf Spee*, in the cruiser *Königsberg*, and in the torpedo boat *G10*. The results achieved varied. The longest distance that could be measured by radio was twenty miles, a range at which a target could difinitely be detected. When World War II broke out, there were in practice only three German ships with radio detecting and ranging apparatus at their disposal, and these three vessels were, of all things, training ships.

The Father of Radar

In Britain the original aim of using radar ranging procedures had been to determine the altitude of certain conducting layers in the ionosphere. These layers had been discovered by the physicist Edward Victor (afterward Sir Edward) Appleton. To reach these altitudes, pulses were sent up perpendicularly into the air by means of suitable antenna systems. If such conducting layers existed, the radio waves must be thrown back to the earth, and an echo, a *radio echo*, would be received. As the velocity of propagation of radio waves was known—186,000 miles per second—it must be possible to determine the height of the conducting layers. It was hoped that their altitude could be calculated from the time taken by the signal and the strength of the echo. Radio echoes were indeed received, and the height of the layers was worked out.

A Norwegian, Fredrick Størmer, had carried out experiments of this kind in the twenties, and the chief result had been the establishment of the altitude of the northern lights. A series of experiments designed to measure the height of the ionosphere had been completed at about the same time by Gregory Breit and Merle A. Tuve in Washington, D.C. The military were not at first interested in these purely scientific experiments.

Serious attention on the part of the service chiefs was first aroused after Robert Alexander (afterward Sir Robert) Watson-Watt, a descendant of the famous James Watt, suggested the possibility of displaying radio ranging signals in a cathode-ray tube and determining their propagation time electronically. The idea was the result of an inquiry by Harry Egerton Wimperis, Director of Scientific Research at the British Air Ministry.

In November 1934 a Committee for the Scientific Survey of Air Defense was established; it was made up of Sir Henry Tizard, Professors A. V. Hill and Patrick Blackett, Wimperis himself, and A. P. Rowe, who later became famous as a designer. It was to consider "how far recent advances in scientific and technical knowledge can be used to strengthen the present methods of defense against hostile aircraft." In this context Wimperis was interested in the possibility of using some kind of damaging radiation—popularly described as "death rays"—against such aircraft. Watson-Watt himself was convinced that producing a weapon of this kind was not feasible. He suggested instead the possibility of harnessing radio waves for the detection and location of aircraft and calculating the distance involved. The committee called for the earliest possible practical demonstration.

The first attempt took place on February 26, 1935, near the short-wave transmitter at Daventry, then the most powerful in Britain. Watson-Watt selected the vicinity of the transmitter because he wanted to prove that aircraft can be located by radio ranging even when the radio on board is switched off during flight. The metal surfaces of the aircraft reflect radio waves in exactly the same way as a ship's side or a conducting layer in the atmosphere.

Watson-Watt arranged for an aircraft to take off and fly up and down the main beam of the Daventry transmitter. Armed with headsets, the experimenters waited for any noise that might be caused by electric currents. Then, at the moment predicted by Watson-Watt, a crackle and rustle actually became audible. The radio waves emitted by the Daventry transmitter were intercepted by the wing surfaces of the aircraft and reflected back to earth. The plane acted like a mirror, a proof that aircraft can be *located* even when their radios are not working or are switched off. This in itself would have caused no surprise if Watson-Watt had not thought up something special. As an extra, he displayed the reflected signal in a cathode-ray tube. The radio beam thrown back by the metal surfaces showed clearly on the picture screen of the tube as a moving light blip.

This was the first radar experiment in history in which a cathode-ray tube was used as an indicator. By means of this arrangement the aircraft could be followed without trouble for a distance of eight miles. The R.A.F. realized at once the great significance of this procedure, and its superiority to all others as an air-raid warning system. If this system were properly developed—if perhaps a whole network of such radar stations could be built along the entire coastline of Britain—any possibility of surprise from the air would be virtually blocked. Watson-Watt now received all the support he needed, but it was laid down that, as far as was possible, the system was to be kept secret. No attacker, no pilot of a reconnaissance aircraft flying at 33,000 to 45,000 feet was to be allowed to know that he was being shadowed by radar before he reached the British coast.

A start was made by erecting five fairly small experimental stations on the east coast of Britain. By the spring of 1936 the 240-foot antenna masts were ready. They were used to send out quite short pulses and pick them up again. The average wave length on which these transmitters operated was just over ten centimeters. In the summer of that same year R.A.F. personnel began training with radar equipment. In 1937 fifteen more radar stations were built, again on the east coast. By this time the first portable radar set had been constructed, and was installed experimentally in an aircraft. By July 1939 Britain's radar stations, now stretching in an unbroken chain from the northernmost tip of Scotland to the Isle of Wight, could locate aircraft at a range of eighty miles. Moreover, the number of aircraft in a formation could be fairly accurately assessed.

The construction of antenna masts, often 350 feet high, along Britain's coast had been observed in Germany with some suspicion. But the Germans at first failed to understand the significance of these antennas. Agents sent in reports of new "directional antennas" and of new ultra short-wave stations, because the wave lengths on which the British were transmitting were of the order of 1.5 to 2 meters. The agents did not know that the British were using these relatively long waves for camouflage. In reality, all the stations were already provided with equipment that enabled them to switch over at a moment's notice to the ultrashort ten-centimeter waves. Nevertheless, the Germans could not fail to suspect that these preparations were concerned with radar, and attempts were made to find out how far the British had progressed.

The energy impulses sent out by a radar transmitter can be monitored only from a position close to it, and even

THE MAGIC OF RAYS   238

then the wave length has to be known. The Germans believed they already knew the wave length: 1.5 to 2 meters.
Suitable monitoring devices were therefore hurriedly manufactured, and a clandestine reconnaissance was ordered.
On August 2, 1939, the airship *Graf Zeppelin* climbed into
the sky for a flight along the British Isles, carrying appropriate receiving equipment. Throughout the flight, experts
sat at their sets and searched one wave band after another.
But not a single suspicious signal was picked up. They
thereupon flew home reassured. What the Germans could
not know was that the British had got word of the planned
reconnaissance; that they had located the airship long before she reached Britain's air space; and that all British
radar stations had then been ordered to observe absolute
radio silence. By this time radar stations in Britain were
manned day and night.

The Plan Position Indicator

With the first radar set installed by the British in an aircraft, friend could be distinguished from foe in the air at a
range of three to four miles and at 200 yards in a lateral
direction. However, the most important development in
radar was the Plan Position Indicator (PPI), a piece of
equipment first put into operational use by the British. This
was an apparatus in which a rotating concave antenna was
used in conjunction with a cathode-ray tube. The principle
of the PPI equipment was roughly as follows. The rotating
transmitted beam swept the area under inspection. On the
fluorescent screen in the cathode-ray tube the observer saw
only a circle of light with a blip. If, however, the beam was
blocked in its path by an obstacle and reflected, a second
blip appeared on the screen. The fluorescent screen was
marked with a grid of circular lines and graduated scales—

for example, twelve circular sectors each representing 100 yards.

It was thus an easy matter to find out where the obstacle struck by the beam was located, and a trained observer could judge from the size of the blips what sort of object was involved. The process was developed by the British and later by the Americans to a point where it could even be used to carry out electronic air reconnaissance. For this purpose an electronic sweep was directed not at the sky but at the earth. The advantage of this was that reconnaissance could be made from a high altitude by night as well as by day and in dense fog. The screen of the cathode-ray tube showed the electronic "air photograph" of the landscape spread out below the aircraft. This procedure could provide very precise indications of the height and depth of imperfectly mapped territory, and could also supply checks of existing data, without any need for survey teams.

If the air space under inspection was empty and free of targets, the fluorescent screen remained uniformly lit. By means of PPI equipment it was possible for crews in England to watch aircraft taking off in Hamburg, regardless of whether they were on a night or a day operation. The radar wave had stripped aircraft of their cloak of invisibility. The first sets of this type were used operationally on October 16, 1940. By Christmas six of them had been completed, and at the beginning of January 1941 the twelfth was ready.

At the same time, all available radio hams and amateurs in Britain were mobilized. They brought with them an asset of inestimable value: radio "know-how," a sixth sense in dealing with highly complicated apparatus. Backed by these enthusiasts, Britain entered the battle for mastery of the air.

About the time when many thousands of British amateurs were flocking to join the radar defense system, the

Telefunken Company in Germany, "on orders from the highest quarter," was obliged to cease operations at its microwave research laboratory. The Würzburg equipment, devised in the summer of 1940, had been so improved that it could be operated in an aircraft, and it now was possible to increase the range of reconnaissance to five miles with a lateral range of 200 yards. Was not the new apparatus superior to the enemy's equipment? Did not the constantly rising figures for aircraft shot down in 1942 demonstrate German air superiority?

After these heavy blows the British shifted their attacking altitude to 40,000 feet and flexed their muscles for the counterblow. One night a British commando unit landed near Dieppe with orders to capture a German Würzburg apparatus. The commandos forced their way to a cycling track that agents' reports had indicated as the site of a Würzburg, overpowered the sentries, seized the apparatus under the very eyes of the crew, and rushed it back to the beach and onto a waiting ship.

The German report spoke of an "abortive landing attempt" that had been "successfully beaten off." The announcement suppressed the fact that in the course of this "abortive landing attempt" one of the few existing specimens of the Würzburg apparatus had fallen into British hands. The captured equipment enabled Britain's technicians to ascertain the wave lengths on which the Germans operated and other important details. The successful British commando raid cost the German technicians and engineers two years of hard work to make up for the blow suffered at Dieppe. Their hopes were pinned on the *Voll-Wismar* equipment, an apparatus that possessed alternative frequencies.

While the Germans were still working on their Voll-Wismar equipment, the British thought of something entirely new. They covered western Germany with an invisible guide-beam system, made up of nothing more than ultrashort waves that were constantly sent out in the same direction in a narrow beam. These waves were always modulated by a single note. The object of the direction beams was to guide bombers to their targets.

The British called the new approach the "Gee" system. It consisted of a grid of position lines transmitted from home bases in Britain over Holland, Belgium, the Rhineland, and the Ruhr. One of the merits of the arrangement was that it greatly increased navigational accuracy and so made possible more concentrated attacks with smaller losses in bombers. It meant that the pilot of an aircraft was no longer dependent upon good visibility, nor was he hampered by cloud or fog. He flew at a prescribed speed and altitude. Everything else was looked after by the anonymous "traveler's guide" sitting at a home air base somewhere in Britain: a man at a desk issuing bombing instructions.

The first flights to the Ruhr area based on this system were carried out in March 1942. The results exceeded all expectations. Blind bombing, guided and controlled by the ultrashort-wave radar spider's web, began its work. The crews of the aircraft involved often did not even know what place they had bombed, and frequently did not find out until they read the newspapers two or three days later.

The first large-scale attack guided by the Gee system was launched on December 21, 1942. The enterprise, called Operation Oboe, was under the direction of Wing-Commander D. C. T. Bennett. The target of the operation was the Krupp works at Essen. The bombing was directed from a desk in the radar laboratory at Malvern College.

As soon as the bomber squadrons had been given the order for take-off, the blip on the radar screen at Malvern began to move. It was created by the bomber formation that would now fly from the British Isles toward the Continent and Essen. The formation had to fly exactly 262 miles along the guide beam. Its flying speed was to be no more and no less than 250 miles per hour. The weather and wind reports continually pouring into Malvern College were immediately evaluated and allowed for in the calculations. It became apparent from these that the force would have to be given a 1,650-yard lead angle if the bombers were to register direct hits on the Krupp works in the target area. Here, too, the system came through the test with flying colors. When the blip on the giant fluorescent screen stood at 260 miles, Wing-Commander Bennett pressed a button, interrupting the humming note by which the bombers had been guided. This was the prearranged signal for the bomb bays to be opened, the signal to "release bombs." Yet neither Bennett nor the bomber crews could say at that moment whether it was Essen, Duisburg, or Gelsenkirchen that had been hit. Not until the following day was it learned from reconnaissance that half the bombs had fallen on the Krupp works and caused immense devastation.

The Gee system made it possible for bombers to resume operations on any day at the point where they had left off the previous day. This was the start of "carpet bombing," by means of which one "carpet" of bombs was dropped next to another.

The Mystery of the Metal-Foil Strips

On July 24, 1943, the first formation of R.A.F. bombers flew over the big Hamburg flak tower at 11:25 p.m. The radar crews studying the Würzburg equipment in operation there reported "enemy aircraft at an altitude of 10,500 feet." And this was the last piece of information they were to give out that night.

A moment later the fluorescent screen in the tower showed thousands and thousands of blips; the picture screen was covered with flickering points of light. What did this mean? If there were as many aircraft in the air as there were blips on the screen, then the air fleets of the entire world must be over Hamburg! From bunker crews and air-raid warning points, reports poured into the control center, all of them asking the same questions: "What is wrong? Our sets are showing too many blips. They are not working any more. What are we to do?" When the control center realized that the picture was the same everywhere, the order went out to "switch off equipment." With those words the air watch over Hamburg was eliminated and the antiaircraft defenses no longer had target data. The flak gunners were compelled to shoot blind in the vague hope of scoring a hit.

What had happened was this: Several hundred tons of small strips of paper with a silvery gloss had been dropped, with the bombs, at various points over the city. They were made of thin aluminum foil glued to pieces of paper and slightly folded lengthwise. No one in Germany knew their purpose. As soon as the first strips were found, the air-defense experts gave orders that they were not to be touched because they were probably poisoned.

Not until much later did the population learn that these strips were a countermeasure against radar—the simplest countermeasure imaginable and, theoretically, known to German physicists. A six-ounce bundle of 6,000 strips looked to radar like three heavy bombers; the radar beam was deflected by the strips exactly as it was by the metal surfaces of aircraft.

Ironically, a small quantity of such strips had been prepared in Germany during the Battle of Britain, to paralyze the British radar network; but the battle had been lost before they got as far as operational use. And then the device was simply forgotten until that July night when more than 800 bombers attacked Hamburg unmolested and almost without loss. Each of the aircraft emptied up to two tons of the feathery metal-foil strips over the target area.

The Magnetron

As early as 1910 Otto von Bayer had succeeded in producing electric waves only two millimeters in length—a record that stood until 1923. Then a spark-discharge apparatus working on Hertz's principle was used to excite wave lengths of between 0.9 and 0.2 millimeters. The shortest electromagnetic wave yet produced has a wave length of 0.09 millimeters. It is excited by what is called a *mass radiator*, a device consisting in essence of a metal drum filled with fine metal filings which is set in motion and rotated. If an alternating voltage is applied to the drum, tiny sparks flash among the metal filings, exciting electromagnetic waves of the length in question.

During World War II German experts were in agreement that wave lengths of less than ten centimeters were not suitable for radar purposes, and all experiments along these lines were brought to a halt. The British possessed an apparatus they called H₂S, the "radar television set"—later named the "Rotterdam" apparatus by the Germans because they succeeded in salvaging one such set from a British aircraft shot down near Rotterdam. The set was so heavy —about 1¼ tons—that it could be accommodated only in certain types of aircraft and, in fact, was installed only in "Pathfinder" planes.

The British "Gee" system had disadvantages. The guide beams transmitted from a British air base reached no farther than the Ruhr area. To enable the R.A.F. to penetrate farther into Germany, it was arranged that certain aircraft should themselves carry equipment that could send out guide beams. Having located the target, these guides, or "Pathfinders," then pinpointed it with "markers" for the mass formations following them. On the area marked off by four markers the bombers then dropped their "carpet." The latter term was used because bombs were dropped practically side by side, so that the over-all pattern resembled a carpet. It can be safely said that it was the British H_2S equipment that decided the air war, and later the submarine war, in favor of the Allies. The apparatus, then the most advanced in the world, contained a *magnetron* of extremely high power, and carried an additional fifty tubes in its metal housing.

What is a magnetron? It is a special kind of transmitting tube which generates very short electromagnetic waves. The magnetron used by the British was no bigger than the sound box of a phonograph, and had an output power of 800 watts. In principle, the tube consists of a hot filament (cathode) placed in the middle of a tubular anode. A powerful magnetic field running parallel with the hot filament and the axis of the anode tube prevents the electrons leaving the hot filament from making for the metal anode by the fastest possible route. Instead, they are forced into a circular path or, better still, into a cycloidal path. If the magnetic field is very strong, the electrons are unable to reach the metal anode. In that case, of course, no anode current is produced. If, however, the magnetic field is so regulated that the electrons can hit the metal anode, the full anode current suddenly sets in. This strong, sudden anode current at once reacts on the electrons in its turn, immediately cutting off the flow of current again. This is the effect for which the magnetron is designed.

In this border zone—no anode current, full anode current—electric oscillations are created in much the same way as in a normal transmitting tube. The wave lengths obtainable in this manner are appreciably shorter than those produced by transmitting tubes of normal design, and the generated power is greater. Even the early models were able to produce fifteen-centimeter waves. To achieve still shorter wave lengths, M. L. Oliphant proposed a new device: the *cavity magnetron*.

Eight symmetrically arranged holes were bored into a flat block of copper and linked, by small slots, to a center hole of fairly large diameter. The hot cathode filament was placed parallel to the bore of the center hole, so that the electrons could stream from it to the anode. Coming under the influence of the magnetic field, they were deflected from their straight path and guided past the narrow slots. The process might be compared to what would happen if we tried to whistle a tune on a hollow key. By blowing across the aperture we should set up a strong oscillation in the hollow of the key which would become audible as a whistling note. The oscillations created in one of the cavities of the *cavity magnetron* induce similar oscillations in the adjoining cavities, and this causes a crescendo of ultra-high-frequency electromagnetic oscillations. The oscillation frequency in such a device is of the order of three billion per second, corresponding to a wave length of ten centimenters. That is by no means the shortest wave length that can be achieved with a magnetron of this kind. Even before the war ended, it was demonstrated that a wave length of five millimeters can be obtained without difficulty.

The magnetron in the "Rotterdam" equipment operated on a wave length of nine centimeters. The German anti-radar experts had not known this wave length was being used, and only when the wreckage of an H_2S set was salvaged were they able to reconstruct the design and wiring of the apparatus. But an effective device to counter the "Rotterdam" equipment, the *Berlin* apparatus, could not be put into serial production until 1944. By that time it was strategically obsolete.

The Moon Echo

The scientists and technicians who developed radar during the war rendered an inestimable service to research.

When the war ended, long-deferred problems could be approached with the most advanced radar equipment.

One such undertaking involved using radar to break through the conducting layers of the ionosphere in order to reach the moon. Could the necessary energies be generated and the rays be so narrowly beamed that they could get to the moon, and would the energy bounced off the moon suffice to bring the rays back to earth? These questions were the objects of an interesting experiment carried out on January 10, 1946, in the grounds of the Evans Signal Laboratory at Belmar, New Jersey, by a number of American physicists and technicians, using a special radar transmitting and receiving apparatus. The reflector constructed for the purpose consisted of a horizontal directional antenna with an edge length of thirty-three feet, and consisting of eight horizontal and eight vertical dipoles. It was set up on a 100-foot tower. The equipment operated on a frequency of 113 million cycles per second, corresponding to a wave length of 2.65 meters. The transmitter was used to send out short impulses lasting approximately one tenth to one half of a second in the direction of the moon. They actually reached the earth again, though at very much lower strength, 2.4 seconds later, as predicted. In that time the transmission beam had covered a distance of roughly 450,-000 miles. The returning radar beam was observed and recorded acoustically by means of a loudspeaker and optically by a cathode-ray tube.

Radar observation of meteors and meteor showers has since become a regular practice. The radio echoes so obtained do not come from meteor bodies, which are often minute, sometimes smaller than a cherry stone and therefore unlikely to be located by radar beams. However, these tiny fragments of planetary matter ionize the air, and it is this process that can be demonstrated to have taken place. How well the procedure works is shown by the fact that some four to ten times as many meteors are discovered by radar signals as are located optically by telescope.

In the course of radar-equipment tests in the United States during World War II a peculiar fact was observed which led to an entirely new application of short waves. It was found that radar beams with a wave length of approximately three centimeters were greatly weakened as soon as mist or fine drizzle raised the humidity in air to a very high level. It was not realized until later that the waves in question caused the tiny droplets of mist to oscillate, and that in the process the entire energy of the radio beam was consumed. This was obviously a case of *resonance absorption*. Was it not an excellent means of determining the size and arrangement of atoms in molecules? the researchers asked themselves. It proved to be just that. First, interesting information was obtained about the ammonia molecule; then other substances were examined with equal success. It became evident that research into matter could be carried out much more accurately and with much greater certainty by *microwave spectroscopy* than by light spectroscopy.

At the same time another fact came to light. It had originally been thought that electric waves are reflected only by metal. The researchers were therefore astonished when they received radio echoes from droplets of mist or water, and even from fine dust particles. The strength of the reflected beam was found to depend on the mass of the particle and its size. The character of the radio echoes varied according to whether it was raining slightly or more heavily, snowing or hailing, or whether a sandstorm was on the way. So consistently was this true that it soon became possible to make predictions. These discoveries encouraged meteorologists to use radar beams to follow certain types of weather over great distances. Today radar meteorology is applied to the study of weather as a matter of course.

The equipment available for this purpose enables weather

conditions to be accurately read on the screen of a cathode-ray tube. Storms, gales, squalls, showers, hurricanes, typhoons, whirlwinds, and waterspouts present quite characteristic pictures that an expert can easily interpret. Showers appear as rather bright, nebulous patches of indefinite size with fuzzy edges. Squalls show a very similar picture, but their boundaries are more firmly outlined; usually they take the form of strips moving more or less rapidly across the picture screen. Storms show a dense, brightly luminous core with sharply defined edges. Hurricanes and typhoons are recognizable by their dark "eyes" —blots with jagged projections. The direction and distance of the various meteorological phenomena can be worked out by means of graduated circles on the screen. Radar meteorology operates chiefly in the three-to-ten-centimeter wave band, which corresponds to a frequency of 10,000 to three billion cycles per second.

The Astronomer's Ear

Every radio technician knows that at a certain level of amplification a rustle is heard which is caused by the movement of electrons in the tubes. The sound of electrons emerging from the glowing hot filament (cathode) and their impact on the grid and the anode of the tube become audible. If we disregard these tube noises, a residue of noise energy is left whose source remained a mystery for a long time. Strangely, this noise is particularly distinct in the short- and ultrashort-wave bands. What causes it?

It had already been proved by Heinrich Hertz that light and the electric waves he discovered were akin to each other. But if radio waves and light are related, if they differ only by reason of their wave length, why should it not be possible for the sun to emit radio waves? The first researcher to take up this question was Sir Oliver Lodge. Between 1897 and the turn of the century he carried out a series of experiments in Liverpool to prove the existence of such radiation. In keeping with the resources available at the time, his experimental facilities were meager, but the difficulties he worked under were greatly increased by the exceptionally high noise level. Any radiation that might exist was bound to be blanketed by the crash and crackle of atmospheric discharges. At all events, Lodge was unable to detect any radiation, but he firmly believed it was there. He therefore recommended that similar experiments be carried out in areas with a lower noise level, preferably in the countryside. However, his recommendation was not acted upon, and not until many years later did someone, by pure chance, hit on the right lead.

In 1942 a British radar unit scanning the sky for German bomber squadrons in the Liverpool area picked up some peculiar "radio signals." They were static noises that attained their greatest strength when the antenna was pointing directly at the sun. If the antenna was turned elsewhere, these curious signals disappeared. It was recalled that similar signals had been picked up in 1930, but the matter had not been pursued.

At that time Karl G. Jansky, an American radio specialist, had picked up these rustling noises whenever his antenna was directed toward a particular point of the compass. Jansky had suspected that this interference radiation originated in the Milky Way, and though his view had at first met with disbelief, his observations had later been checked by many people and confirmed. Was it possible that stars were responsible for this noise? Was it really a fact that, in addition to light and heat, stars gave off radio waves on a wave length that had been found to be five meters? In 1936 H. Fränz of the Telefunken Company had succeeded in identifying radio waves from the sun with a wave length of twenty-one centimeters, but apparently these experiments had remained unknown to the British.

We receive from the sun and the fixed stars not only ultraviolet, visible, and infrared light but also waves of considerably greater length. They are waves that come within the scope of the short- and ultrashort-wave band—waves varying in length from a few millimeters to several hundred meters. This cosmic radio radiation travels through space virtually without loss of strength. Any disturbance or weakening it suffers as a result of mist, rain, and clouds is negligible, so that we can be said to receive radio waves just as they were emitted from the surface of the sun. In many cases they are our only source of information concerning remote stellar systems from which no light rays have so far reached us, though these radio waves have accomplished the journey. How does it come about that a star—or any radiant body—emits, in addition to ordinary light rays, waves that belong in the radio band?

If we look into a tube that is closed at the end, the whole interior of the tube appears to us to be black. If we heat the inside of the tube, we obtain *cavity radiation*, or *black-body radiation*, and we are able to identify with great accuracy each of the waves emitted. It becomes evident from this that radiation from a source with a temperature of about 6,000 degrees centigrade, or approximately 11,000 degrees Fahrenheit (the temperature on the surface of the sun), does not consist only of heat and light waves. It contains, over and above these, short and ultrashort waves belonging in the radio band. We may accordingly picture our sun as such a source of black-body radiation. In the case of the sun, the maximum amount of radiation falls within the range of the optically visible rays, but in addition considerably longer waves occur. They reach far into the range of the medium, short, and ultrashort waves. Certainly the intensity of the sun's radiation in the medium-wave range is extremely low: for a wave length of approximately 300 meters, it is no more than 0.8 of a watt. That is the total transmission power of the sun in the *broadcast-wave band.* In the case of three-centimeter waves, our sun becomes an ultrashort-wave transmitter with an output power of 8,000 kilowatts. When sunspots occur, this power can be considerably increased. At times of intensified sunspot activity an output of a million kilowatts and more has been recorded. In the face of power of this order, the strength of our high-power short-wave stations is completely swamped.

Since it became known that the sun and fixed stars emit radio waves of varying lengths, scientists have begun a systematic search of the heavens. Special apparatus has been developed, and giant receiving antennas have been erected for the purpose in various countries. The largest *radio telescope* in the world to date, at Jodrell Bank Experimental Station in Cheshire, England, has a reflector 250 feet in diameter.

Antennas of this size are used to pick up radio waves coming in from interstellar space. The waves are reflected onto a central receiving antenna at the focal point of the parabola. From here the impulses are carried to a special receiver, amplified, and then detected either acoustically by a loudspeaker or optically in a cathode-ray tube.

How extremely sensitive the operation of such equipment can be is made clear by the fact that various paraboloid antennas are automatically controlled by the incoming radio waves. In other words, the instant the radio waves arrive from outer space, the antenna automatically turns in the direction of their incidence. Subsequently the antenna continues to swivel in the direction of the cosmic source of radiation—some star or other—until the latter has dropped below the horizon. Such equipment has picked up radio waves that had been traveling for more than 75,000 years before they reached the earth. The received power of these signals from outer space is sometimes no greater than one micro-micro-micro-micro-watt ($= 10^{-24}$ watts).

Searching space with this apparatus, we have stumbled

upon stars that emit nothing but radio waves. The most interesting radio-star radiation to be encountered so far comes from the W-shaped constellation Cassiopeia. The star in question, previously not seen but only "heard," was actually identified as a tiny point of light in 1951 by the Mount Palomar telescope. In the meantime many others have been discovered. However, the most notable result achieved by the young science of radio astronomy is the realization that our Milky Way system rotates in the manner of a lawn sprinkler. This knowledge was derived from overlap phenomena observed in the behavior of incoming radio waves.

CHAPTER 10

From the Nipkow Disk to the Television Set

ONE DAY DURING the 1928 Radio Exhibition in Berlin a man about sixty-five years old turned up at the stand of a well-known German company and started studying the television receivers on display there. As the man was obviously familiar with many of the details of the apparatus, the attendants took him for an enthusiast who liked tinkering with sets. But when he began to talk to them, asserting that he, Paul Nipkow, was the originator of television—that the disk which formed the heart of the television apparatus on display was his invention—they took him for a demented crackpot. An altercation developed, and finally the old man was asked to leave.

There was truth in his claim, however, and the fact that his pioneer invention was the result of a chance observation cannot detract from the legitimacy of his claim.

One night late in 1883 Paul Nipkow, born in provincial Lauenburg and then an impecunious student at Berlin, was toying with a circular cardboard disk in which, just for fun, he had bored a series of holes, arranging them—by intention or intuition—in the form of a spiral. While he was playing with the disk—he had stuck it on a knitting needle and given it a jolt to make it spin—he realized to his astonishment that he could "scan" pictures with it. For instance, if he held the revolving disk up toward the Christmas tree in the room and looked at it, the lighted tree suddenly appeared in the spiral cutout formed by the holes spinning around. This observation sparked an idea in Nipkow's mind.

He knew that a simple selenium cell—invented three year earlier by Charles Sumner Tainter—could convert light into an electric current. In those days a cell of this kind was very primitive, consisting of a film of selenium brazed between two wires of platinized silver. As soon as one of these cells was exposed to light, the electrical resistance dropped and the current increased. The current developed was strong or weak, according to the brightness of the light involved.

If a picture could be broken down with the aid of a perforated disk into picture dots, and the light passing through one of the holes were guided onto a selenium cell, a current varying in strength with the brightness of the light coming through would result, and this current could be carried by wire anywhere one liked. (The possibility of wireless transmission did not occur to Nipkow because electromagnetic waves were not discovered until five years later.) If he could conduct this current by wire to a receiver in which the electric impulses could be reconverted into light dots, he might be able to realize the "miracle of seeing at a distance."

Nipkow lost no time. On January 6, 1884, he took the specifications for his "electrical telescope" to the Patent Office in Berlin; his fiancée had lent him the small sum for the registration fee. The patent was granted him on January 15, 1885, no objection having been entered during the intervening twelve months. But his invention, however well de-

vised, had been made "too early"—that is, before the discovery of radio waves and the invention of amplifier tubes.
Nobody in Nipkow's native Germany—or anywhere else,
for that matter—was willing to sink a single cent in the
proposition. Paul Nipkow had to watch his patent lapse
after only a few years.

Television was Born in an Attic

If you have an opportunity to visit the Science Museum
at South Kensington in London, your eye may be caught by
a case containing the most venerable relics of British television: some perforated disks of the kind Nipkow had constructed, two small electric motors, and—a doll's head.
This is the original "Televisor" apparatus built by John
Logie Baird, self-styled "manufacturer and inventor."

The son of a minister, Baird was born in 1888 at Helens-
burgh, Scotland. He was so frail a child that his parents considered him not strong enough to attend a school, and tu-
tored him at home themselves. A curious incident made
them aware of his interest in, and precocious talent for,
electrical engineering.

When twelve years old, he decided to lay a private "telephone line" with three extensions. The cables required were
quite arbitrarily pulled from one window to another
through trees and across streets. Soon he was able to com-
municate on this line with some of his playmates. One night
one of the cables broke, a man driving a cart got caught in
it, and in his efforts to free himself from the tangle of wires
he tore his coat. He demanded compensation from the National Telephone Company, and an examination of the
broken "line" revealed young Baird's illicit telephone
enterprise. His father is said to have given him a sound
thrashing.

After graduation from Lachfield Academy, John Baird

went to the University of Glasgow. At the outbreak of World War I he volunteered for service, but was rejected on account of a weak heart, shortsightedness, and generally poor health. Lacking other opportunities, he took an engineering job with a power station, but routine work did not satisfy him. He had found out that a paper wrapping kept his feet warm even in severe winter; he quit his job and began to manufacture "health socks" out of crepe paper, only to sell the business soon, with another "company" he had established for the manufacture of a special shoe polish thrown in. Then he opened a jam factory on one of the West Indian islands, where he had gone shortly after the end of the war for reasons of health, but this venture miscarried too, and in 1922, after a severe bout of malaria, he returned to Britain. Almost penniless, without a job, and still feeling quite ill, he kept his head above water in London by selling a batch of jam he had brought back with him. At that time he invented a glass razor supposed to enable men to shave without first soaping their faces. "Balloon shoes" were another of his inventions. Nothing came of any of them, and eventually he moved to the seaside town of Hastings, where he took an attic room at a boardinghouse to devote himself to practical work on a notion that had been exercising his mind for quite some time—the idea of a television apparatus.

He was perfectly clear in his mind about the principles involved. He had tinkered before with selenium, the element with which a light ray could be transformed into an electric current; he also had fashioned a device that automatically switched on the electric light when a room grew dark. He knew all the possibilities of television from German, French, and American patent specifications. But none of these patents had ever been put to the test.

Baird began to rig up apparatus with what amounted to a lot of scrap material—old bicycle wheels, hatboxes, some sealing wax, string, an antiquated army transmitter, and an old electric motor. The most important part of his ramshackle equipment was, of course, the Nipkow disk.

Baird's disk was made of cardboard and had holes in the usual arrangement, each of them in continuity with the preceding ones. With this disk Baird found it possible to break down a picture into individual dots. To this end, an object— a flower, let us say—had to be illuminated by a strong light. If now the disk was rotated in front of the flower, the light reflected by it passed through the holes of the spinning disk and fell on a photoelectric cell in which the light was converted into a current. The greater the amount of light passing through one of these holes, the stronger was the current so created. In other words, the current set up varied with the intensity of the light.

To convert the picture thus "scanned" into visible form again, it was necessary to convey the current to a suitable receiver. This, like the transmitter, consisted of a Nipkow disk and a driving motor. The only difference was that a glow lamp now operated in the place where the photoelectric cell had been. The lamp reacted to slight fluctuations of current, and its glow therefore matched the intensity of the current, a weak current producing a dimmer glow than a strong one. Thus, the impulses coming from the transmitting station were here converted into light impulses. That was the principle on which the young inventor built his system.

His first "live" experiments miscarried. Some friends he had invited to his place to be "televised" sat for hours in front of his apparatus, submitting patiently to beams of klieg lights. But only some flashes of light and some shadows appeared on Baird's small picture screen. The ridicule he was subjected to caused him to turn to an inanimate object for his experiments—an old doll's head, as it happened. But these tests did not come off either. Something like a silhouette did show up, but the image was still hopelessly blurred. He now decided to use an even simpler image—a white cross on a black ground. And at last the cross came up quite clearly!

Now Baird invited some London newspapermen to Hastings for a demonstration. But only one of them, F. H. Robinson, a reporter specializing in technical matters, published a factual story. In the April 3, 1924, issue of the periodical *Radio-Cinema* he described his visit to the "laboratory" of Mr. John Logie Baird, who, as his demonstration had shown, had made progress on the way to "radio-vision." In fact, Mr. Baird's invention seemed to be exploitable commercially, its cost amounting to about £40. The inventor was of the opinion, Robinson concluded, that there were no further obstacles to having moving pictures transmitted by wireless.

When this report failed to evoke any response, Baird tried to find a financial backer by advertising in the dailies. A certain Mr. Day, owner of an electrical-appliance store, turned up and offered Baird the sum of £200 against a thirty-per-cent share in the profits. As soon as the deal was closed, John Baird, who meanwhile had married, left Hastings for London, where in two small rooms he continued his experiments.

In the summer of 1925 he met a son of Gordon Selfridge, the department-store owner, and that young man suggested to Baird that he demonstrate his invention, for a small fee, three times a day in the radio department of the store. Although the inventor realized that his apparatus was not yet ready for public display, he agreed to the proposition, which also provided that he would be supplied free of charge with all the parts he required. He installed himself at the store and began his public demonstrations. A handout distributed by the management admitted that Mr. Baird's invention was still imperfect—the pictures lacked definition and flickered—but the public was reminded that Edison's phonograph at its initial demonstration had been even less perfect than the instrument now on view in the

showroom. Selfridge's, the handout added, was sponsoring
Mr. Baird's demonstrations to offer the public a chance of
witnessing the first performances of one of the great inventions of the century.

Perhaps the store had expected its general business to
profit from the demonstrations and these hopes had not
materialized. At any rate, after two weeks Baird was asked
to dismantle his equipment. To add to his plight, his partner
threatened him with litigation. At the height of his extremity some of his relatives came to his aid so that he could
free himself from the most pressing of his financial obliga-
tions.

What worried the undaunted inventor most, even at this
nadir of his career, was the fact that the picture on the
screen had remained fuzzy and indistinct throughout his
demonstrations at Selfridge's. One day in October 1925
Baird, again working with his white cross on a black
ground, accidentally brushed against one of the scanning
disks with his sleeve—and for a split second the cross
seemed to come up with sharp clarity on the picture
screen! He had not been mistaken: by slowing down the
disk once again with his hand, he obtained excellent pictures. This chance occurrence made him realize that the
transmitting disk and the receiving disk must revolve at the
same speed. In other words, the disks must be synchronized
before good pictures could be achieved. Baird at once co-
ordinated the two rates of revolution, then exchanged the
cross for the doll's head, and, lo and behold, the head appeared clear and distinct on the screen.

Now, he felt, he must have a human face on that screen.
He went out to get hold of someone at once. The first person he ran into, an office boy, reluctantly followed Baird
and allowed himself to be sat down in front of the weird
apparatus. At first the picture was still somewhat distorted
by black stripes, but Baird at once realized what caused

them—an inaccurate disposition of the holes in the disk. He easily made the necessary alterations and "televised" the boy with clarity.

Three weeks later, on January 27, 1926, forty prominent members of the Royal Institution squeezed their way up the narrow staircase to the inventor's rooms. The gentlemen had come to determine whether there was anything in his new apparatus. One of them, J. D. Perry, summing up his impressions in a memorandum, described how vision took place by means of a disk containing a lens; gas-filled potassium cells were used as photoelectric cells; synchronization —the co-ordinated operation of the two motors—was achieved by linking the two machines. As his light source the inventor used very bright spotlights, which he placed as close as possible to the object. Perry regretted that he could offer no data concerning the amplifier system because no sketches had been provided and Baird refused to reveal any details.

Although Baird's invention now rapidly became known, the "experts"—in this case, the heads of the British Broadcasting Corporation—were not interested in this "sensational development." Baird therefore decided to strike out on his own and, having secured financial backing, founded a company. Very soon afterward he succeeded in transmitting pictures between London and Glasgow, and somewhat later he transmitted pictures to a receiving station on the liner *Berengaria* when she was on the high seas. The ship's chief radio operator was highly astonished when he suddenly saw the face of his fiancée smiling at him and talking to him from the picture screen. Baird had invited her to his London laboratory and transmitted her face from there.

Only in 1928 did the BBC in London decide to make tests with Baird's apparatus. A 1.5-kilowatt transmitter was placed at his disposal for half-hour periods after broadcasting hours. The tests went off to Baird's utmost satisfaction.

The "Wonder Tube"

At the 1930 Berlin Radio Fair a sound film was being shown on a television screen; there was a do-it-yourself television kit to admire; and at one stand people could talk to someone by telephone and see him at the same time on a screen. But there was nothing to suggest that all the television apparatus shown at the fair would be hopelessly out of date within less than a year.

In the United States the first television play had just been produced; three television cameras developed by the Swedish-born American Ernst Frederick Werner Alexanderson shot the scenes at a range of ten feet while the actors almost wilted away under a battery of powerful klieg lights. By that time, however, a number of great technologists—among them, the Russian-born American Vladimir Zworykin and the young American Philo Taylor Farnsworth—were already working on the development of devices that were to set the pattern for electronic television scanning.

On the night before Christmas Eve in 1930 some reporters were invited to the radio station of the Post Office in Berlin "to be shown something new." What they were to see was a completely new type of television apparatus that bore no resemblance to the old designs.

All it consisted of was a type of cathode-ray tube with an enlarged picture screen. This tube made possible picture reproduction of a quality never before achieved with any television set. It had three essential features: an almost completely evacuated glass bulb ending in a broad butt, a hot filament that supplied the electrons, and a fluorescent screen that lit up as soon as it was hit by electrons. The stream of electrons, which came like a cloud off the white-hot filament, was drawn out into a narrow beam by a small sheet-metal cylinder when a negative potential was applied to the latter. At the same time, the beam could be easily steered by this device. If the potential was altered, the effect on the beam was to raise or lower the number of electrons reaching the fluorescent screen. Bright and dark dots of light—for that is how the electrons hitting the screen appeared—produced a tolerable picture if only they were composed fast enough.

But how were the dots to be composed at such a rate that the eye failed to observe the deception that was being practiced on it? The speed at which the writing electron beam was guided across the screen had to be very great. Above all, suitable luminescent substances had to be found. They must have a brief period of afterglow because that was the only means of preventing the picture from becoming blurred and indistinct. The tube was equipped with a magnetic deflection system to bring the beam back to the left for the next line after each journey from left to right. At first this deflection system was very crude, but it was a promising beginning.

"On the screen of the tube," a German reporter wrote at the time, "we saw a bluish-white picture of those familiar young ladies in bathing suits. . . . The picture quality is better than one gets with receivers using the Nipkow disk."

Soon there were picture tubes with which 10,000 picture dots could be achieved. Yet the apparatus was so small that it could be accommodated on a desk. There was no longer a distracting motor, no disk that had to be driven, and no arc lamp that gave off intolerable heat. The main component was the tube, the "wonder tube," which would easily fit into a briefcase.

This was the end of the Nipkow disk, the Weiller drum, the mirror cell, the Kerr cell, and numerous other ingenious devices that had been thrown up in several countries by the search for a mechanical framework for television. This was the beginning of the new kind of television, described earlier, which was to supplant Baird's apparatus.

As time went on, the comparatively simple "wonder

tube" developed into a veritable technical marvel. But today's ultimate peak of knowledge, reflected in complicated instruments, may be out of date tomorrow.

Index

12734

A NOTE ABOUT THE AUTHOR

JOHANNES DOGIGLI was born in 1915 in Traunstein, Bavaria. He was educated at the Munich Polytechnikum and the Technische Hochschule of that town. For several years he worked as an electrical and radio engineer with Siemens Halske-Schuckert. Since 1956 he has been one of the editors of Oldenbourg Verlag, a hundred-year-old German publishing house that specializes in books on scientific and technical subjects.

Mr. Dogigli has published three previous books, and is a regular contributor to international science journals and to popular magazines. Married and the father of two children, he lives in Munich.

January 1961

A NOTE ON THE TYPE

THE TEXT of this book was set on the Linotype in
JANSON, a recutting made direct from matrices long
thought to have been made by Anton Janson, a
Dutchman who was a practicing type-founder in
Leipzig during the years 1668–87. However, it has
been conclusively demonstrated that these types are
actually the work of Nicholas Kis (1650–1702), a
Hungarian who learned his trade most probably
from the master Dutch type-founder Dirk Voskens.

Composed, printed, and bound by KINGSPORT
PRESS, INC., Kingsport, Tenn. Paper manufactured
by S. D. WARREN Co., Boston. Typography by
VINCENT TORRE.

SOUTHWEST MIAMI HIGH SCHOOL